A PRACTICAL GUIDE TO MANAGING PANIC AND PHOBIA

KEVIN GOURNAY

ASSET BOOKS

A catalogue record for this book is available from the British Library.

ISBN 1 900179 03 2

Printed and bound in Great Britain by Hobbs the Printer Ltd

CONTENTS

PREFACE

I feel highly honoured and proud to have been asked to write the introduction to what I consider to be both an excellent and an important book about overcoming anxiety disorders. As both a recovering agoraphobic and the Chief Executive of a charity, *No Panic*, which seeks to use self-help as a method of overcoming anxiety disorders, I have long felt that there was a huge need for a definitive book on tackling and beating panic and phobias, written by a professional in a way that is both accessible to sufferers and carers and simple to follow. This, undoubtedly, is such a book.

I have known Professor Gournay, since 1982, initially as a therapist who helped me to successfully overcome my first period of agoraphobia and, subsequently, as a patron of *No Panic* of which he is the guiding light. He always told me that he could not overcome my phobia for me but that I must do it for myself. What he did do was to show me how. By following the ideas, suggestions and advice he presents in this book you can do the same.

From those early days, Kevin Gournay has progressed to being one of the world's leading authorities on the treatment of anxiety disorders. He has successfully guided thousands of sufferers along the road to recovery; his methods are proven to have a high rate of success. His advice and suggestions are not 'things' he has read from a manual. Instead, he has been 'out there' with sufferers, gaining experience and insight from working with 'live' subjects. As a non-sufferer, he has an amazing empathy with sufferers and carers. He understands their feelings and their suffering; this puts him in a unique position to help people with these very disabling conditions.

While Kevin earns his living from helping people to overcome anxiety disorders he also devotes much of his spare time to voluntary work, such as his role as a patron of *No Panic*. Without his support, guidance and enthusiasm, our charity would not be the success it is today. I would also stress that the motivation for this book came from his caring nature which makes him want to help others. So read what he has to say, and give his ideas a try. Don't just take my word for it; you have nothing to lose and everything to gain!

Kevin looks at the whole picture related to anxiety disorders, such as diet, medication, exercise, etc., and examines the whole body concept which is of great importance in both overcoming the problems and maintaining your recovery. Many other books on this subject have failed to address these issues; sufferers consequently miss out on factors that can have a huge impact on overcoming their anxiety. He also stresses that, in an ideal world, all sufferers would have access to professional help but, as this is probably too much to hope for, we can do much to help ourselves. After all is said and done we have got to 'cure' ourselves. Don't sit around thinking that you can't do it without professional help. Do it!

Finally, I would like to pay tribute to Kevin's reference to and advice to carers. So many authors ignore their role in the recovery programme and the pressures to which they are subjected. This book is very positive about the part they have to play and shows how, in many cases, they take over the role of the professional.

Thanks for writing the book Kevin, I am sure many more sufferers and carers will benefit from your endeavours.

Colin M Hammond,
Chief Executive, *No Panic*,
Telford, May 1996.

FOREWORD

There have been several sources of inspiration for this book. Firstly, I have been involved in treating anxiety states for over 20 years and, for 15 of these, in research into these problems. During this time it has become clear that the practical information and advice conveyed through self-help books can be invaluable in helping sufferers to manage their own condition. Indeed, I know of several such books that have helped patients considerably more than any professional therapy. My aim is not to duplicate effort but to add to the array of material already available. In some ways, I believe that the more the better and that sufferers of anxiety states often need to look at the same material put in slightly different ways to help them to clarify its meaning and to help them to achieve the best results.

In my clinical practice, I am constantly faced with patients who have, for one reason or another, been starved of information. Sometimes, although they have seen numerous psychologists, psychiatrists, nurses and other counsellors, they have never been given comprehensive information about the state(s) from which they suffer. I hope that this book may go some way to remedying this and complement the endeavours of the professionals. However, I also realise that information put in the right way can sometimes replace the need for professional help and, if this is so, I will be very pleased.

Another source of inspiration for this text has been my long association with Professor Isaac Marks, originally my teacher at the Maudsley Hospital in the 1970s. Isaac has helped literally thousands of people, either directly as a therapist or indirectly through the scores of health professionals he has trained; latterly his efforts to help people to help themselves have also been important. Without doubt his book, *'Living with Fear'*, first published in 1978, was the 'mother' of all self-help texts about anxiety. Isaac's contribution to clinical practice and the education of both health professionals and patients is undoubtedly second to none. His research on self-help persuaded me that this should perhaps be the first line of approach and that, at times, self-help in all its various forms can be much better than professional treatment. The simple reason for this is that giving people the means to help themselves keeps the problem within their control. There is nothing worse than being treated by a therapist who thinks they know best!

My association with *No Panic*, which I joined as a patron when it was first formed in 1989, has been another source of inspiration. The Chief Executive, Colin Hammond, still speaks to me on the telephone several times a week and, like Isaac Marks, has given a great part of his life to helping others. Colin, himself a sufferer of a very severe form of panic disorder and agoraphobia, knows only too well the pain and distress of the anxiety they cause. Indeed, it was he who first suggested that I should write this book and, although the time between his initial suggestion and publication is five years, he has, throughout that time, continued to remind me of my duty!

This text is designed to provide information about the various anxiety states, to say what they are and how commonly they occur. I will then try to describe, in the most balanced way that I can, the methods of treatment available and to look at the current research. The second section concentrates on self-help providing suggestions that sufferers can try, if they wish, to fight the symptoms and handicaps.

It must be said at the outset, however, that anxiety is part of the human condition; there are no simple answers for anxiety states. Sufferers often seek a panacea and the complete abolition of their symptoms. Unfortunately, such panaceas do not exist and those who claim total cures (or even 95% success rates!) must be viewed with deep suspicion. There is no defence against some sorts of anxiety; the illness of a close relative, the rebellion of a teenage child, moving house, problems at work, an aggressive neighbour, the hole in the ozone layer, may all cause anxiety for some people. Sometimes these causes cluster together producing an anxiety so overwhelming that we cannot cope.

In my view, therefore, some of these conditions are normal and we must beware of over-professionalising the help that is needed. In my research I have noted, like many others before me, that two-thirds of patients get better in time without any professional treatment. On the other hand, it is also known that a large proportion of an entire generation has been, or is currently, addicted to minor tranquillisers and, perhaps, as many people again have become dependent on therapists of one sort or another. This does not mean that sufferers should be left to their own devices; I am merely cautioning against over-optimistic claims and against sufferers being persuaded to embark on a programme of treatment without due consideration being given to the much wider context.

In summary, therefore, this book is written primarily for sufferers of anxiety and not for therapists and other professionals. These people may well find some of which I have written useful, but the content is unashamedly practical rather than theoretical.

Kevin Gournay
London, April, 1996.

To Siobhán, Alex, Sam and Frankie

CHAPTER 1:   CATEGORIES OF ANXIETY STATES

Anxiety states can be classified in many different ways and, even among professionals, there are different classification systems. In practice, however, the list that follows probably represents a reasonable way of categorising various anxiety states:

- Panic disorder
- Panic disorder with agoraphobia
- Agoraphobia
- Specific (simple) phobia
- Social phobia or social anxiety disorder
- Post-traumatic stress disorder
- Obsessive compulsive disorder

and   • Generalised anxiety state.

This book concentrates mainly on panic disorder and phobias. I have decided to tackle them together because of the considerable overlap between these conditions. Most sufferers of phobias will report panic attacks at some time and most people who have panic attacks over a long period will report some degree of avoidance or phobic behaviour. Furthermore, some people can suffer several of these conditions at the same time.

Although this book does not focus on either post-traumatic stress disorder (PTSD) or obsessive compulsive disorder in any detail, as both these topics deserve attention in their own right, some of the material that follows will be applicable to these conditions. For example, sufferers of PTSD will often report considerable levels of panic and be phobic of situations linked to the triggering event or avoid situations reminding them of the original trauma. Thus, for example, people who have developed PTSD after experiencing a car crash, may begin to avoid all situations related to public transport as well as travelling by car. The principles of treatment and self-help will be exactly the same for such people as for those whose phobias and panic were not caused by a specific triggering event. However, many people with PTSD will often need a range of other behavioural and cognitive behavioural treatments to treat the other wider symptoms of the condition.

Although children's fears and phobias are probably best treated in a separate book, the central principles of managing phobias and panic attacks in children are the same as those that apply to adults. Unfortunately, services for children with fears and phobias in the UK are often woefully inadequate and, at best, most districts can only offer family therapies or traditional psychoanalytically-oriented therapy for children with problems.

It seems a great pity that the simple and very effective behavioural procedures of anxiety reduction that are described here are not more widely available to children and adolescents. One wonders how much adult suffering could be spared if the appropriate interventions were given during childhood. Thus children, or parents of children, who suffer should apply as much of the advice that I offer to adults as possible.

Panic disorder

Panic is a very difficult concept to define adequately. One of the problems is that everyone is different and what is experienced as a panic attack by one person may 'simply' be a very high level of anxiety for someone else. Perhaps the best working definition of panic is that which describes the condition where, in the mind of the sufferer, the anxiety has become uncontrollable. The American

Psychiatric Association, in their Diagnostic and Statistical Manual (1994) has defined panic as *a discreet period of intense discomfort in which four or more of the following symptoms developed abruptly and reached a peak within 10 minutes'*. These symptoms are:

1. Palpitations, pounding heart or accelerated heart rate
2. Sweating
3. Trembling or shaking
4. Sensations of shortness of breath or smothering
5. Feelings of choking
6. Chest pain or discomfort
7. Nausea or abdominal distress
8. Feeling dizzy, unsteady, light-headed or faint
9. Derealisation (feelings of unreality) or depersonalisation (feelings of being detached from one's self)
10. Fear of losing control or going crazy
11. Fear of dying
12. Numbing or tingling sensations
13. Chills or hot flushes.

Many sufferers of panic attacks know that these symptoms can come not only in fours but also in fives, sevens and even thirteens! This means that the possible combination of sensations and thoughts that can occur during attacks of panic is enormous.

Panic attack sufferers will know that a combination of symptoms makes them feel that something dreadful is about to happen; the feeling of loss of control is perhaps the most central preoccupation for most people. Panic can be such a distressing feeling that the lives of many sufferers become dominated, not by the panic itself, but by the fear of the panic. This fear of fear then begins to form a pattern of preoccupation that may lead sufferers to adapt their lives in a wide variety of ways so as to deal with the problem.

Some sufferers experience phases when the panics come with some considerable ferocity and then seem to go away for no particular reason. Some of the causes of panic discussed below may give a clue to why this fluctuating course can occur. However, during phases when panic attacks are common, sufferers will very often experience considerable life disruption. Panic attacks that occur over a long period of time can have a variety of distressing consequences.

Having panic attacks day in and day out, as is the case for some people, can lead to feelings of dejection and physical exhaustion and, eventually, the sufferer may develop depression. This state is characterised by feeling that there is no escape from the problem and that life is not worth living. A significant minority of people with panic disorder may then go on to develop a serious depressive illness that will, in turn, lead to increased susceptibility to panic attacks.

Another consequence of long-term panic attacks can be a reliance on drugs and alcohol. Alcohol seems to provide an instant solution but, if overused, can of course lead to serious problems in its own right. A special section is devoted to consideration of the use of alcohol (page 84-87) as my own research, conducted some years ago, showed that one in five people suffering from panic attacks and agoraphobia were using alcohol at dangerously high levels. These findings were confirmed by similar studies carried out in the United States.

It also seems clear that, for a minority of people who develop both a drinking problem and agoraphobia, withdrawing alcohol leads to disappearance of their phobic state.

Agoraphobia

The word 'agoraphobia' was originally coined by Westphal, a German neurologist, more than 120 years ago to describe a condition that he had observed in four men. Since then there have been many descriptions of this condition and other names have been attached to it. For example, another German neurologist - Benedikt - used a word that literally translates as 'dizziness in public places'; it has also been called *peur d'espace*, phobic anxiety depersonalisation syndrome and some American researchers have also labelled the condition as endogenous anxiety! However, 'agoraphobia' essentially describes a specific anxiety that occurs in places or situations where the person perceives that escape might be difficult or embarrassing or that help might not be readily available.

In general terms, those with agoraphobia suffer from a number of fears that may include, for example, being away from home, being in a crowd, travelling on public transport, being in a car, standing in a queue, crossing a bridge, and so on. Some sufferers only experience panic attacks when confronted with these situations or in anticipation of entering them. Others, however, may also experience recurrent and unexpected panic attacks that seem to occur spontaneously. Thus, sometimes, sufferers can be sitting at home quietly watching television or undertaking relatively relaxing activities when feelings of panic develop, sometimes gradually, sometimes abruptly.

When panic attacks are not linked to a phobic situation, and occur at frequent intervals, the condition is called panic disorder. If the person also suffers agoraphobic fears, this condition is sometimes called panic disorder with agoraphobia. However, to complicate matters further, many people with agoraphobia may have fears that are not connected with specific situations such as exposure to public places. For example, many sufferers have concerns about their physical health so that their panic attacks may be triggered by thoughts of illness and death. Thus one can often trace the source of a panic attack to a specific trigger even when, at first sight, it seems to have occurred without specific reason. This may be a trivial physical symptom or other bodily sensation although some sufferers may develop panic attacks after watching a TV film on an illness theme or reading a newspaper article about someone contracting a fatal disease.

Agoraphobia usually starts in early adult life with most cases beginning between the ages of 20 and 30 years. Sometimes, problems start very suddenly but often the condition develops in a very slow and gradual way with increasing avoidance growing over many years. There is no doubt that it can cause widespread life restrictions and lead to secondary problems such as poor self-esteem, marital disharmony and depression.

Sufferers from agoraphobia, like those experiencing panic attacks, often experience a wide range of symptoms of anxiety that may continue, in one shape or form, between panic attacks and exposure to situations away from a secure base. Such symptoms include palpitations, sweating, dry mouth, over-activity of the gastro-intestinal tract and physical shaking. Hyperventilation or over-breathing (see page 69) causes additional symptoms which can be very frightening. These include pins and needles or tingling, yawning, sighing, feeling light-headed and faint, feeling unable to breathe and, in some cases, muscle spasms.

Phobics often worry about a sudden loss of control, going mad or fainting, running amok, vomiting, becoming incontinent of urine or faeces, dying during a panic attack or having a heart attack or stroke. Most sufferers know that their fears are irrational but, nevertheless, when panic attacks come or when they are faced with the situation that brings on their fears they can do little to rationalise them and escape seems the only way out.

In addition to the specific fears, most agoraphobics would describe themselves as 'natural worriers' and often anticipate, with anxiety, all kinds of life events. Some agoraphobics are particularly preoccupied about their health while others may be prone to obsessional rituals and ruminations.

Up to 5% of the population may have significant agoraphobic difficulties and as many as one in eight of us may have one or two agoraphobic fears. Although women outnumber men several times in those referred for medical treatment, it is known that there are many more men with the problem than outpatient statistics would indicate. This is perhaps because, as research shows, men tend to deny or hide their fearfulness at a much greater rate than women.

Simple phobias

Simple phobias are extremely common and I agree with the suggestion that having one or two phobias is virtually normal and that nearly everyone has something that they fear and are inclined to avoid.

A phobia can be defined as a marked or persistent fear that is excessive or unreasonable or out of keeping with the danger that the situation or object presents. There is usually a considerable amount of anticipation when one is aware of a potential contact with the feared object or situation. However, once that object or situation has been removed, or the person 'escapes', the anxiety level returns to normal. Although the cause of phobias is not fully understood it does seem that repetitive escapes make the fear worse.

However, the sufferer is aware that the fear associated with virtually all specific phobias is excessive and/or unreasonable and this often leads them to report that they feel silly or embarrassed in admitting to such a problem. Virtually every object or situation you can think of can become the object of a phobia in some individuals. Phobias of small animals are particularly common; unlike agoraphobia, these fears tend to start in childhood.

Some specific phobias, such as fear of vomiting or incontinence, may be linked to other conditions, such as obsessions and agoraphobia. These fears can become really extensive and, in the case of both vomiting and incontinence phobias, may lead to a lifetime of misery caused by the avoidance and preoccupation that occurs. For example, someone with vomiting phobia may well have to adapt their eating habits so as to avoid certain foodstuffs and I have several times heard of people having to discard a whole week's shopping because of fears of contamination. Such fear may spread much more widely to include not just the checking of food, but also a pre-occupation with their children's health, the possibility of infection through exposure to crowds and the avoidance of alcohol because of the possible nausea and vomiting that this could produce.

Fear of incontinence may lead to what is, in effect, agoraphobic avoidance when people often need to avoid or substantially modify various journeys because of the need to be sure that they have access to public lavatories. Some of those with this fear will go as far as wearing nappies or incontinence pads and sufferers usually have a great sense of shame about their problems.

For example, I recall seeing a patient some years ago who had become addicted to an old-fashioned diarrhoea remedy that contained morphine. He felt that the only way he could prevent his fear of incontinence coming to fruition was to take large quantities of this substance and thus remain in a state of constipation. This unfortunate man then waited until the week's work was complete to take a laxative which would ruin his weekend because of the severe diarrhoea this caused; he would then begin to take the anti-diarrhoea remedy again on Monday morning. Although this is an extreme example it is certainly not unique and it demonstrates the dramatic way in which some people will modify their lives so as to accommodate their phobia.

Likewise one often sees people with bee and wasp phobia who will completely avoid their garden and only go out after dark in the summer months. There are also patients who never go to the theatre or cinema because of their fear of bangs and loud noises, people who will never take their children into the park because of a fear of dogs or the numerous people I have seen who avoid coming into the centre of London, not because of a fear of crowds but because of their phobia of pigeons.

Blood/injury phobia

There is one specific phobia that is worthy of mention because it is, in some ways, very different from other such phobias. A fear of blood is quite common and most of us will know someone who faints at the sight of blood or during an injection. This specific phobia, sometimes called a blood/injury fear, produces a physical response that is quite different from that associated with other anxiety and phobic states.

In all such states, save for blood/injury phobia, the response is an increase in arousal with an associated increase in heart rate, blood pressure and respiration. Although many sufferers fear that they will faint or pass out during an anxiety attack, this is probably the least likely outcome. In a state of high anxiety the blood pressure is increased and so that oxygenated blood is transported to all parts of the body and, in particular, to the vital organs, such as the brain, the heart and the liver. Fainting, on the other hand, is the body's response to a lack of oxygenated blood in the brain, usually because of low blood pressure; fainting simply helps to restore the blood supply to the brain because, if you are flat on your face, the blood from the heart does not have to work against gravity! Fears of fainting are, therefore, very irrational.

However, in blood/injury phobias, the body produces a paradoxical response when someone is exposed to blood or injury or, indeed, injections or the sight of needles. These phobics respond with a reduction in heart rate and an associated reduction in blood pressure that leads to a dramatic faint. Although the condition generally starts in childhood it can sometimes occur in later life and I have certainly come across cases of doctors and nurses who have suddenly developed this strange response to blood and injury. Surprising as it may seem, in at least one of these cases, the sufferer had qualified as a nurse and practised for several years by skilfully avoiding direct exposure to blood. She had even spent twelve weeks in the operating theatre during her training managing to become involved in a range of tasks that enabled her to avoid any actual confrontation with operations and open wounds! Similarly, when working in wards and the casualty department, she managed always 'to find something else to do' when there was a possibility of seeing blood.

This particular nurse gave a great deal of time and energy to caring for the sick and dying but, nevertheless, largely avoided the sight of blood. On the odd occasions when she was confronted without warning she fainted; despite this her problem was never addressed. However, she was eventually faced with confronting her fear after she witnessed a car accident when, because of her phobia, she was unable to assist badly injured passengers. This experience made her realise that she needed to do something about the problem that she had hidden successfully for so long. I am pleased to report that after her brief, but nevertheless somewhat frightening, behavioural treatment she made a virtually complete recovery from the problem that had dogged her for so long.

Social phobias

The American Psychiatric Association's (1994) definition of social phobia is that it is a marked and persistent fear of one or more social or performance situations, in which the sufferer is exposed to either unfamiliar people or to possible scrutiny by others. The individual fears that he or she will show anxiety symptoms or act in a way that will be humiliating or embarrassing. Such fears are extremely common because of their nature (i.e. because they are principally concerned about being humiliated or embarrassed). However sufferers will, by the same token, greatly under-report their fears.

Social phobias can, of course, occur in their own right and the lay person's conception of social phobia as a form of shyness is, in some senses, correct. However, social phobia is usually much more than simple shyness and sufferers may avoid all kinds of social interaction as a result of which their lives become miserable and depression often follows. Many people with agoraphobic fears often also have a marked degree of social phobia and there is considerable overlap between the two conditions.

Because people with such phobias tend to avoid social situations they simply do not get the practice that is required to become socially competent. This lack of practice further inhibits their willingness to enter into interactions with others because of their inability to hold a conversation or perform many of the normal social skills and so compounds the situation. As a result, social phobics may appear to have poor social skills because they do not look you in the eye, they stand awkwardly and the anxiety they suffer reduces the amount of facial expression they use. Thus, when it comes to treatment, many social phobics will require some coaching in social skills in order to help them to overcome their problem.

Post-traumatic stress disorder (PTSD)

Most people think of PTSD as a condition that is related to major disasters, such as the sinking of the Herald of Free Enterprise or the King's Cross Fire, or linked to combat situations, such as the Vietnam or Gulf War. In fact, such disorders are very common in the general population and it is estimated that up to one in ten of us will experience some symptoms of this condition at some time in our lives. For example, nurses, policemen and firemen often witness sudden death and various tragic events, often involving loss of life or mutilation and, as a result, may develop distressing symptoms. Post-traumatic stress disorders can be suffered by people involved in road traffic accidents, by those who are victims of crime and, unfortunately, by growing numbers of women who report having been raped.

The medical definition of post-traumatic stress emphasises that the person has been exposed to a traumatic event in which they experienced, witnessed or were confronted with an event or events that involved threatened death, serious injury or a threat to the physical integrity of themselves and others. The response to these events usually involves not only a sense of shock and profound fear, but also a sense of helplessness. The event is remembered in graphic detail, often described as being 'in slow motion'. The definition used by doctors and researchers makes it clear that it is not just being involved directly or, indeed, suffering a serious injury, but that witnessing a traumatic event or thinking that you are about to be killed or seriously injured can be sufficient to cause the problem.

Post-traumatic stress disorder comprises of a range of effects. Very often sufferers experience recurrent and intrusive recollections of the event, often in dreams but, sometimes, affected individuals complain of flashbacks that occur during the waking state. Any confrontation with circumstances that remind them of the original event, for example, driving close to the site of the original accident, may cause considerable distress that, in turn, leads to avoidance. The person may experience a numbing of their general responses and show a markedly diminished interest in their usual activities. Sufferers very often complain of feeling detached or estranged from others and they may see no future for themselves.

There is often a range of symptoms including sleep disturbance, irritability or anger, and finding it hard to concentrate. At the same time, affected people become constantly aware of any possible danger in the environment. However, the most common symptom of post-traumatic stress disorder is anxiety that is all-pervasive and is coupled with an avoidance of many varied situations. As is the case with most phobias, the anxiety and avoidance grow, very often leading to even greater depression.

Post-traumatic stress disorder often leads to an excessive use of alcohol and, these days, other non-prescription drugs. This substance abuse is simply an attempt to numb the distress that people feel.

There is absolutely no doubt that post-traumatic stress disorder is an under-recognised condition that needs specialist treatment. Further description is out of place in this text; the subject deserves attention in its own right.

Obsessive Compulsive Disorder

Obsessive compulsive disorder (OCD) will be the subject of another book in this series but is mentioned here because it is one of the anxiety states that often leads to attacks of panic and phobic avoidance.

OCD can take many forms but essentially consists of either intrusive, repetitive and distressing thoughts, or compulsions such as hand washing or checking or repeating an activity. More often than not sufferers experience both of these phenomena and some of the commonest obsessions are linked to a fear of dirt or germs, or of simply doing things 'wrong' or imperfectly. A 'dirt and germs' phobia can lead to repeated hand-washing and sufferers can sometimes take hours to ensure that their hands are perfectly clean. The sufferer is, however, never happy with the end result and the interminable vicious circle commences again.

Sometimes sufferers are afraid of losing control and this is often linked to obsessional and intrusive thoughts regarding the consequences of such a state. As a result, even the kindest and gentlest person may begin to worry about a loss of control that may lead to a violent act, or a deeply religious person may fear shouting out a blasphemy or obscenity in church. Needless to say, these fears never come to fruition. However, sufferers are often completely overwhelmed by their anxieties and depression is very common in the most severe cases. It is a common condition, which affects up to 2% of the population, and we now know that many people with phobias and panic disorder are also affected by OCD.

On a more optimistic note, the behavioural treatments developed for OCD over the last twenty years have brought real hope for sufferers, and treatment approaches are developing all the time. This once terrible, untreatable condition can now be helped by both professional and self-help methods and some of the treatment principles described later in this book can be applied to OCD sufferers with equal success.

Generalised anxiety state

Most of us know the feeling of excessive anxiety or apprehension about an impending family event or a change at work. However, generalised anxiety disorder differs markedly from this and is a term reserved for those whose excessive anxiety and worry develops to such a degree that it interferes with various aspects of their life.

The six central symptoms which are common in generalised anxiety states are:

- Restlessness

- Being easily fatigued
- Difficulty in concentrating or mind 'going blank'
- Irritability
- Muscle tension
- Sleeplessness.

Generalised anxiety disorders can cause impairment of social, occupational and other areas of function and often progress to feeling downright depressed and dejected. While some people are, in a sense, 'born anxious', and may have a life-long tendency to anxiety and worry, some generalised anxiety states are triggered by life-events such as stressful jobs, poor relationships and major life changes in someone who was previously of a calm and relaxed temperament.

On occasions, sufferers may experience high levels of anxiety but this does not develop into frank panic. Similarly, although the anxiety can be severe, sufferers carry on with their normal routine and do not attempt to avoid any specific situations. Anxiety states such as these are known to go through phases and, sometimes, sufferers can experience periods of relative calm.

Although the treatments described in this book are specifically aimed at the management of phobias and panic, some of the more general comments regarding exercise, sleep and the use of alcohol may be helpful.

Generalised anxiety states have recently become the target for treatment endeavours by psychologists. Until just a few years ago treatment of such conditions centred around medications of one sort or another. However, it is now accepted that, wherever possible, medication should be avoided as addiction is a major danger.

While there is no magic treatment, the recent developments in cognitive therapy and cognitive behaviour therapy can make a huge difference to the lives of sufferers changing someone who may be overwhelmed with anxiety into someone who remains a worrier but, nevertheless, is not affected in those important social, occupational and relationship areas.

Children's fears and phobias

The first point to be made about children with fears and phobias is that these are probably present to a greater or lesser degree in every child at some point while they are growing-up. It is, therefore, a grave mistake to rush to seek professional treatment. We all know of the toddler who develops an aversion to the noise of the vacuum cleaner or who dislikes sleeping in the dark. Such fears are absolutely normal, and parents are best advised to take a sensible and comforting approach. Thus, the most appropriate strategy to adopt with a child who develops a fear of a certain object or situation is to coax them gently to face up to that object or situation using, if absolutely necessary, the age-old strategy of bribery! Allowing avoidance is a very dangerous strategy and may, in fact, be the most important variable in strengthening a fear.

In some cases of school phobia, the phobia is made much worse by the parent attempting to deal with it by protecting the child from anxiety. The most sensible approach is to coax the child into the situation (i.e. school), and to stay there for a while as the child settles down. However, most parents will know that, sometimes, distressing as it might be, leaving a child crying in the classroom may be what is needed. Those same parents will also tell you that they very often find out that the child stops crying within seconds of their leaving. The parent, however, may be distressed all day long!

The best general advice regarding children's fears and phobias is to assume that such fears are transient while, at the same time, encouraging exposure. We know that the process psychologists call modelling is another important factor. This simply means showing the child that there is nothing to fear. Indeed, children very often learn by watching other children face things; this peer modelling can sometimes be the most potent factor in helping a fear to disappear. Therefore, playmates and brothers and sisters may turn out to be the best therapists!

Summary

This chapter has addressed a variety of anxiety states and phobias and has highlighted the wide range of physical symptoms that they may cause. It has shown us that phobias and avoidance behaviours are very common and that they may cause considerable life disruption undoubtedly affecting general well-being and quality of life. No-one is immune and we may all be affected by such disorders at some time in our lives. For some of us this will be a 'passing phase'; for others this may be a distressing and disabling condition.

The next chapter will consider how these conditions arise and explore the possible causes before moving on, in the rest of the book, to consider how they can be managed by either professional or self-help methods.

CHAPTER 2:   CAUSES OF ANXIETY AND PHOBIAS

The simple answer to the question of causation is that nobody can really provide a definitive account of how anxiety and phobias arise. That is not to say that there is not a great deal of research that helps us to see how some factors may be implicated in the causation of these conditions but the truth is that there is no single all-embracing theory. In the due course of time some of the research referred to below may clarify the situation considerably, but I think that the only certainty is that there will never be a single comprehensive theory that covers everyone and their particular condition.

Various new technologies have provided major advances in many areas. For example, we can now see the brain much more clearly than previously when we only had conventional X-rays at our disposal. Computerised techniques, augmenting the use of X-rays, enable the production of very clear pictures of the brain. However, these scans (computerised axial tomography (CAT) scans) have now been superseded by Magnetic Resonance Imaging (MRI) scans which have clarified this still further and enable in-depth study of the brain.

Furthermore, it is now possible not just to have very detailed pictures but also to study the brain while it is working by using radioactive isotopes to enable detection of the chemical changes occurring during its metabolism. This so-called functional brain imaging allows researchers to examine the brain while the patient performs various tasks or is exposed to various anxiety-evoking situations. Such research has now shown clearly which areas of the brain are implicated in anxiety and seems to suggest that the brains of those suffering from anxiety states may differ in subtle ways from those of so-called 'normal' populations. This, in turn, points to the possibility that anxiety may be genetically determined and the study of genetics has been greatly enhanced by the use of the new DNA technologies.

These new approaches are, of course, being applied to other conditions, such as cystic fibrosis and muscular dystrophy and, throughout the world, researchers are involved in a major collaboration known as the 'Human Genome Project' designed to identify the complete human genetic structure.

With regard to specific findings in anxiety disorders, we are now fairly sure that there is a substantial genetic component to panic disorder, agoraphobia and obsessive compulsive disorder. It is impossible to predict just how much the children of sufferers of anxiety disorders are at increased risk of suffering from these conditions. Overall, however, although there are some very interesting findings, we are still unable to explain the precise cause(s) of many of those conditions.

Recent research seems to confirm the long-held view that most people with anxiety states are, in some way, biologically predisposed to become more aroused and, therefore, simply 'pump out' more adrenaline than others although the reasons for this are not known. This pre-disposition appears to be inherited although the way in which this occurs, and the proportion of the off-spring who might show this trait, are far from clear. It seems that this tendency may combine with other factors that occur during childhood and, later in life, trigger a clinical state.

As the tendency to produce adrenaline is undoubtedly determined by genetic factors the long-term hope is that treatment based on genetic engineering will modify the specific genetic response concerned. This is probably a real hope for discovering a cure for these conditions. However, it is likely that it will take 10 to 20 years to develop such treatments.

Sometimes, when listening to the history of someone with an anxiety state, it becomes clear that their anxiety has commenced after a specific trauma. For example, the patient may have been involved in an accident or been trapped in a lift; they may have developed their problem as a response to a sudden bereavement or a separation. In such cases, the person may or may not have a predisposition to anxiety. What is interesting is that people who suffer similar traumas often react in very different ways; some develop problems that may persist in the long-term while others endure their experiences with no particular difficulty.

In clinical practice, however, I, like most clinicians, cannot see any clear causation for many of the cases that come to my attention. The patient may say that they have 'not liked' closed spaces but then, at some point in their lives, this dislike gradually developed a greater and greater prominence. Eventually the person suffered a panic for no apparent reason in that situation and then began taking steps to avoid further exposure. The panic attack may happen when the person feels particularly vulnerable. It is also not clear why panic attacks spread to other situations for some people while others continue to feel fear in that situation and that situation alone.

Cognitive psychologists are now looking at the impact of an initial panic attack on future behaviour. There seems to be little doubt that learning to react in an anxious way is, for some people, the most important aspect of the way that their anxiety develops. However, this does not apply to all sufferers thus highlighting once more the tremendous variation that exists in the causation of these conditions. Finally, social factors are of great importance in the way that anxiety states evolve. Some years ago I conducted some research on sex roles and agoraphobia. Not surprisingly this work confirmed the long-held view that women are more predisposed to developing conditions such as agoraphobia because of their social role. Thus dependence on others may be more acceptable in women than men. Furthermore, some male spouses may actually encourage an increased dependency on the part of their partner.

However, my research also showed that, although many more women than men attend for treatment, there are many men who will not admit their fearfulness. While these men do not come for treatment they often seek a solution to their problem by an excessive use of alcohol. Other social factors which cause an increased vulnerability to anxiety are, understandably, poverty, social isolation and unemployment.

Yet another social dimension that has been extensively explored in depression is the role of social support. George Brown and Tirril Harris, two researchers in the Institute of Psychiatry and Bedford College (London), investigated the role of social support in depression finding that those women who had close confiding relationships were much less vulnerable than women without such support structures. Research in anxiety disorders indicates that the same is true for these conditions as for depression and the very positive effects of social support are an excellent reason for encouraging the use of self-help organisations.

In summary, therefore, anxiety, panic and phobias develop in different ways in different people. There is clear evidence that biological, psychological and social factors are all important in causation. However, the precise contribution of each of these factors is still far from clear. It may also be that, in conditions such as panic disorder, the condition in one patient is primarily caused by biological factors (e.g. an excessive production of adrenaline) while, in another patient experiencing the same symptoms, the main cause may be the memories of a trauma from many years ago.

Everyone involved in helping those with anxiety disorder, from the health professionals to the volunteers working for self-help organisations, must recognise that there is probably no single cause for anxiety states. In the majority of cases one has to look at the condition from several perspectives. Doubtless the future holds considerable promise but it seems extremely unlikely that the cause of anxiety will be determined adequately in this generation or, indeed, in several generations to come.

CHAPTER 3: TYPES OF PROFESSIONAL TREATMENT

Apart from self-help, which will be described in some detail later, there are essentially three methods of treating panics and phobias. These are:

1. Psychotherapy (including all forms of insight-oriented methods and various 'talking treatments', including counselling)
2. Drug treatments
3. Behaviour therapy and cognitive behaviour therapy (including exposure therapy).

As self-help is largely based on behavioural and cognitive behavioural approaches there will, inevitably, be some overlap between the discussion of professionally-administered therapy and that of self-help.

1. Psychotherapy

One of the difficulties regarding psychotherapy is its very definition. For many years, psychotherapy largely meant treatments based on the principles of psychoanalysis and, of course, on Freud, Jung, Klein and others who were the main theoretical sources. In its original form, such therapies often took many years and sometimes involved the patient seeing the therapist up to five times a week.

The theory behind psychotherapeutic treatments is essentially that the symptom is merely the product of an underlying conflict that often has its roots in childhood. I will not attempt to provide an overview of the theory of psychoanalytic treatments here, suffice it to say that these supposed conflicts are very often linked to the psychoanalyst's ideas about childhood development. Indeed, it is important to note that psychoanalytic theories have never been proved.

The immediate difficulty associated with the psychoanalytical explanations of a variety of mental health problems is that they largely ignore any possible biological underpinnings of the problem; they also overlook the many and varied social factors that may be partly responsible for the cause and which may substantially maintain the difficulty over the longer term. Even when a basic cause in childhood or adolescence can be uncovered, another major difficulty is that of treating the current problem that may have been present over a number of years and which, in a sense, by that time maintains itself.

I accept that childhood experiences are important. Indeed there is a body of research evidence that shows that people with agoraphobia may have had traumatic separation experiences during crucial parts of their development. However, even in such cases, this cannot be seen as the definitive reason for people's current anxieties. For example, while one person who has been subjected to a traumatic separation goes on to develop agoraphobia in adult life another person who has exactly the same experience, grows up to be resilient, independent and positively non-phobic.

Modern forms of psychotherapy come in various 'packages' and presentations. For example, some therapists still maintain a close adherence to the traditional theories of psychoanalysis, while others say that they are much less influenced by the dim and distant figures of Freud and Jung. Among modern day psychotherapies one finds a wide variety of approaches and, for the researcher, the main difficulty is that most of these are impossible to define; there are, however, one or two notable exceptions. The main problem for both researchers and consumers is that there is usually no answer to the question of whether the therapy has been subjected to a properly controlled research trial. Unfortunately, many therapists defend this lack of evidence by saying that it is impossible to consider human beings together and that each case must be examined individually.

There is, of course, a basic truth in the differences that exist between human beings. However, human beings also have a great number of similarities and it *is* possible for a skilled researcher to investigate human responses while controlling both similarities and differences. Examples of this are seen all the time in general medicine and, of course, individual's bodies vary in the same way as their minds. This variation has not, however, stopped medical researchers from evaluating the effects of specific drugs in treating a variety of conditions knowing that, for example, people with cardiac problems may experience various individual factors that may or may not lead to cardiac disease.

Counselling is often considered to be something different from psychotherapy. However, both counselling and psychotherapy are essentially methods that involve discussion of the supposed origins of the problem and/or maintaining factors. Furthermore, the theoretical underpinnings of counsellors are very often the same as those of psychotherapists. Although I have been involved in research into psychological treatments for 20 years I still can't tell the difference between the various forms of counselling and the various forms of psychotherapy and I find it difficult to follow the arguments that suggest there is a difference between them.

Again counselling is something that usually defies evaluation because of the reluctance of counsellors to enter into the rigours of scientific trials. There are, however, some in-depth studies of counselling and the results are, overall, very disappointing for counsellors. For example, some researchers (e.g. Professor Greg Wilkinson of the University of Liverpool) have considered the collective outcomes of studies of counselling concluding that, overall, it has no more than a placebo effect. This is not to say that all counselling is completely ineffective but rather points to the current situation where it is being used as a treatment on very large numbers of people in perhaps an indiscriminate and ineffective fashion. Indeed, Professor Wilkinson, and some of my colleagues at the Institute of Psychiatry, have recently examined the effectiveness of very specific counselling methods with selected populations and the results are very encouraging. This work entails helping the sufferer to acquire skills in problem solving and limits the counsellor input to six sessions. However most counselling offered in the UK is very unfocused and may be without limit of time.

Over the past few years increasing numbers of General Practitioners (GPs) have employed counsellors to help deal with the considerable problems of depression and anxiety suffered by the population at large. To illustrate this point, several pieces of research have shown that up to 40% of those attending a GP for consultation for physical problems also suffered some depression, anxiety or difficulty with relationships. Indeed, I conducted a large study of the counselling carried out by community psychiatric nurses in GPs' surgeries over a three-year period. Most of these nurses had considerable experience and had received training in various forms of counselling over and above their professional (nursing) training. Although patients clearly valued what was offered a significant number dropped out of treatment. However, the GPs who employed the counsellors thought that they did a wonderful job and many of the patients showed very significant improvements in their symptoms.

I studied a group of people with anxiety and depression who a GP wished to refer to counsellors allocating them at random either to counselling or to a waiting list, where they received no treatment, with the expectation that they would receive treatment later on. Those on the waiting list were all offered counselling some months later but, while they were waiting, they continued to see their GP or seek whatever other help they wished. All patients saw a researcher who did not know who was seeing a counsellor and who was on the waiting list. A standard interview procedure and administration of various tests of anxiety, depression and social functioning enabled us to determine the patients' emotional and mental state. As we had anticipated, patients who were receiving counselling improved. However, patients on the waiting list improved to almost exactly the same extent. This indicates that many problems will get better in the due course of time and that professional treatment of this sort (counselling) does not necessarily have any effect. I must stress, however, that the patients who entered this study were suffering from generalised anxiety and, depression, conditions that are notoriously susceptible to spontaneous improvement.

However, panic and phobias are very different. If they have been present for some months, the trend is that they will continue unabated unless treatment is sought. Indeed, numerous studies have shown that, while psychotherapy had no effect on panic and phobias, behaviour therapy led to excellent outcomes.

To return to my research, it was interesting to note that, at first sight, the counsellors appeared to be doing a wonderful job and saving the GPs valuable time. However, when we conducted a very careful analysis of the extent to which health care resources were consumed by the patients, including how often they attended their GP, how often they went to see other specialists and so on, we found surprising results. Those who were seeing a counsellor consumed exactly the same health care resources as those who were not; the rates of GP consultation were the same for both groups! This example shows that one must always be suspicious of drawing conclusions about cause and effect and, at the end of the day, one must rely on standard scientific approaches, such as the randomised controlled trial, to help ascertain what is real and what is apparent.

Another difficulty with psychotherapy, to which I will refer again below, is that the qualifications and backgrounds of psychotherapists and counsellors vary considerably and sometimes even experienced professionals have difficulty deciding whether the people who offer these services are properly trained.

2. Drug treatments

Three broad categories of drugs may be prescribed for those with anxiety disorders (i.e. tranquillisers, antidepressants and beta-blockers).

a. Tranquillisers

By the late 1980's some 26 million prescriptions for tranquillisers were issued each year in the UK and their use was so common that it was estimated that one woman in three over the age of 40 years had a regular prescription in any one year. One of the reasons why drugs such as Valium and Ativan (i.e. benzodiazepines) were so widely used is that they are, in the short-term at least, very powerful anti-anxiety agents and anyone who has had an intravenous injection of Valium at the dentist will know that it can be very effective at calming 'the nerves'. Furthermore, every clinician knows that there are some patients who may use a drug like Valium once or twice a year to help them when flying or visiting the dentist; these people, who would normally experience great anxiety when doing such things, are able to undertake these activities in a relaxed state.

The great difficulty with such drugs is that they can quickly cause addiction and their actual effect on anxiety can wear off after literally a few dozen doses. This has led British doctors to be very reluctant to prescribe them. However, in other countries, and particularly in the USA, such drugs are still widely prescribed and advocated for some forms of anxiety state. There is, quite clearly, a place for the occasional use of such medication in acute episodes of anxiety but clearly its use must be carefully monitored. Such drugs must be prescribed and monitored by someone who has specialist experience.

It is my belief that, save for acute crises, these drugs should not be prescribed for anxiety states of any sort because of the dangers of addiction. I also believe that the research evidence for their long-term effectiveness is very poor. I am also cautioned by my memories of the advertising material for Valium in the late 1960s that claimed that it was a drug without side-effects and so was safe for all to use! Similar claims had been made for the barbiturates many years before and although, like the benzodiazepines, barbiturates can, in the short-term, considerably reduce anxiety, the problems of addiction turned out to be the same.

Drug companies are beginning to market new forms of tranquilliser that are claimed to be effective in the treatment of anxiety but which have none of the risks associated with the benzodiazepines. While I welcome such developments, and feel that, in the long-term, drug treatments may have something substantial to offer, I cannot but feel that we must be cautious in their use; the problem is that it often takes many years before the truth about the safety of a drug emerges.

b. Antidepressants

A variety of antidepressants is available that can, broadly, be considered in terms of three groups including monoamine oxidase inhibitors and the tricyclic antidepressants.

Monoamine oxidase inhibitors (MAOI) are not now prescribed very often although some sufferers are still taking them after many years. They were developed shortly after the second World War and became notorious because of their incompatibility with certain food substances such as cheese, red wine and beef extracts. Anybody taking these drugs must carry a card that warns of the various adverse reactions and side-effects. These include insomnia, skin rashes, impotence and a range of other symptoms but, more worryingly, if these drugs are mixed with the foods described above there may be a dangerous increase in blood pressure that, in some cases, may cause a stroke or heart attack. Understandably, therefore, many doctors are now reluctant to prescribe such drugs.

Over the years there have been many claims and counterclaims about the possible dangers associated with MAOIs although there are still a number of psychiatrists who claim that they are very effective in the treatment of anxiety and depression. However, the evidence for their effectiveness is, at best, sparse. Some years ago I examined this in a review of published literature and found that, although there was some evidence of short-term symptom relief, all well-controlled studies pointed to no real long-term benefits.

Anyone offered these drugs should satisfy themselves that there is a good reason for taking them. My simple advice is for you to question the prescriber as to their safety and the evidence of their effectiveness in treating your particular condition.

Recently, newer and safer forms of these drugs have been developed and I think that the best one can say is that initial reports sound promising. However, again I think the watchword is caution!

Tricyclic antidepressants are the second group of antidepressants, and are, at present, probably the most widely prescribed of all the antidepressants. Like the MAOI, these drugs have been around for about 40 years. Despite this, the debate about their usefulness continues to the present day. My own evaluation of their effectiveness is that some of these drugs can be effective in the longer-term in patients with some anxiety states, if those patients also have a co-existing depressive illness. However, they are probably much less safe than was previously thought. There seem to be problems of long-term weight gain and, in older patients, there is some evidence that the electrical system of the heart can be affected. At one time it was thought that tricyclic antidepressants could be taken for many years and that addiction was not possible. However, my reading of the current evidence is that some patients do develop addiction to these drugs although the mechanism through which this occurs is unclear. Long-term treatment with such compounds should be avoided unless there is a very good reason for this.

Serotonin re-uptake inhibitors (SSRI's). The third group of drugs, developed in the last decade, contains several sub-groups the most well-known of which are the selective serotonin re-uptake inhibitors (e.g. Prozac). Prozac is fast becoming the world's best-selling drug for the treatment of mental health problems and is seen by many as an answer, not just to mood disorders, but to all sorts of anxiety and, indeed, to personality difficulties.

It must be said that drugs like Prozac have been used by literally millions of people and the scientific evidence is that there is a very low incidence of side-effects. Their efficacy is clear, particularly in the treatment of depression. However, the evidence regarding its effectiveness in treating anxiety states is much less well researched and, again, my personal view is that, although the evidence for this group of drugs is very promising, caution must be exercised in view of the history of other medications.

There are now several new drugs related to Prozac, and other new antidepressants of slightly different chemical makeup, all of which appear to show a lower incidence of side-effects and the evidence for effectiveness seems promising. As mentioned above perhaps, one day, drugs will provide a real answer to panic and phobias, but it is much too early to say that this day has arrived or that Prozac is a universal panacea.

c. Beta-blockers

Beta-blockers are mainly used in the treatment of high blood pressure and, simply, act by reducing the body's state of arousal. Some years ago they were prescribed to reduce the physical symptoms associated with anxiety states. There were early reports that they were helpful in performance anxieties of various kinds. For example, it was found that these drugs assisted with steadying one's hand when engaged in rifle shooting or playing snooker.

Beta-blockers were then applied to more general anxiety states and, over the years, there have been various claims of their efficacy in managing these conditions. However, although they are also widely used in treating panic disorders and agoraphobia, there is very little objective evidence to support their use as a treatment method. In general they appear to treat the symptoms rather than the cause.

Beta-blockers can often cause lethargy and are associated with a variety of side-effects including depression in some individuals, sleeping problems, various bodily sensations such as pins and needles, and a reduction in sexual function. In the short-term, they can make a sufferer feel calm but, unfortunately, in order to maintain this such a high dose is required that the individual will be sluggish and probably much less spontaneous than normal.

3. Behaviour Therapy and Cognitive Behaviour Therapy

Shortly after the War, researchers concluded that the effects of the traditional psychotherapy or drug therapies on anxiety states were poor and so began to examine the field of experimental psychology in attempts to develop alternative treatments. Such researchers saw the development of anxiety as a maladaptive and learned habit and also believed that anxiety states were acquired through a learning or conditioning process.

This led to the development of treatments based on the learning theories of experimental psychology. Thus these researchers believed that a continual process of escape from something that makes you feel anxious strengthens the fear so that a phobia develops. Although this is obviously something of an over-simplification, this approach led to the development of behavioural treatments for phobias, anxiety and panic.

To begin with researchers treated anxiety states by 'de-conditioning' the anxiety response and teaching patients to relax in the presence of the object or situation that normally made them anxious. This technique was called 'systematic desensitisation' or 'psychotherapy by reciprocal inhibition'! Although it had some beneficial effects, researchers eventually moved on to the idea that exposing people to anxiety-provoking situations for long periods of time, in a repeated and systematic fashion, was the most powerful method of treating fear responses.

As Professor Isaac Marks of London's Institute of Psychiatry has repeatedly pointed out, exposure therapy is based on principles that have been around for literally hundreds of years and philosophers, such as Joseph Locke (in his Essay concerning Human Understanding in 1690), advocated exposure as the central method of overcoming a phobia. Indeed, even Sigmund Freud, the archetypal advocate of psychoanalytic treatments, said in several of his works that, once the analysis had worked, the patient needed to face their fear! (This is a liberal paraphrasing of his advice).

By the 1970s, researchers all over the world were beginning to treat patients by exposure methods designed to help them to face up to their fears. However, by this time, the connection between the learning theory of experimental psychology and the real clinical world was becoming much more tenuous. Researchers were beginning to question whether the underlying psychological theory had any relevance to clinical treatment and clinical observations themselves threw into doubt some of the conclusions reached by experimental psychologists in previous years.

Despite some criticism, exposure therapy is now known to be a lasting treatment. For example, although some critics have argued that treating an anxiety state in this simple way would lead to another symptom being produced by the supposed unconscious conflict, this phenomenon (so-called 'symptom substitution') has never materialised. Indeed, evidence from studies that have followed up patients for many years after their treatment shows that the gains of brief simple behavioural treatment using exposure are long-lasting for the majority of patients treated in this way.

People with obsessions and compulsions were also treated by these exposure methods. However, it soon became clear that phobias were somewhat easier to treat than obsessions although, with the right approach and given sufficient time, people with obsessions also showed dramatic improvement.

In the last 20 years, there have been literally thousands of research studies on the treatment of anxiety by behavioural methods as a result of which such methods have gradually become more refined. A growing number of workers now use so-called cognitive methods that involve looking at the thinking patterns of people with anxiety states as habitual responses. Indeed, most people with panic or phobias will tell of thoughts that come automatically and which recur in a habitual fashion. Thus cognitive therapy researchers began to apply the same principles and to develop treatments that focused not just on modifying behaviour but also on modifying thinking that was catastrophic and irrational. It was in this way that cognitive behaviour therapy evolved and is usually employed along with behavioural methods. There is still considerable controversy between researchers about the benefits of cognitive methods but it is fair to say that the consensus is they can add to the efficacy of behavioural methods of treatment. However, there is no-one who will yet argue that there is any substitute for exposure.

Exposure therapy

Twenty years ago, exposure treatments were usually administered by a therapist who spent many hours actually helping the patient enter the real life situation. Indeed, I can remember spending 20 or 30 hours with agoraphobic patients on the London Underground, staying with them until their anxiety reduced. However, it has been shown over the years that, as long as the patient is helped to make the initial entry into the phobic situation, such intensive therapeutic assistance is unnecessary.

Most patients need the exposure principle to be demonstrated by the therapist, thus showing that the anxiety does reduce if one stays in the situation. Once this has been achieved, the sufferer can enlist the help of a family member or friend to help them to apply this consistently over a longer period of time. The purpose of having a therapist or friend around is not for that person to be there permanently but for them to assist in graduating the exposure so that the sufferer faces up to their fear in increasing doses of difficulty.

4. New Treatment Methods

There have been a number of developments in new methods of treatment. For example, some countries have developed approaches dependent upon the use of computer-generated virtual reality. This involves a sufferer wearing a head-mounted display unit through which they are presented with a computer-generated 'world' that changes naturally as their head and/or body move. Some such units also include gloves that allow additional contact with the virtual world. Thus interaction with a virtual environment becomes possible.

Experiments currently being carried out at the Institute of Psychiatry in London are treating spider phobics using this new technology. Thus, instead of having to face the 'real thing', the patient can be exposed to a 'virtual reality spider'. This is obviously a very helpful way of graduating treatment and may prepare the patient for facing the real phobic object with much less difficulty. The applications of this technology will probably be most beneficial for situations that are not readily accessible to patients or therapists in any reliable way. Thus, for example, people with thunder and lightening phobias could be exposed to 'virtual thunder storms' and, indeed, Barbara Rothbaum and her colleagues in Georgia, USA, have recently published a report of the successful treatment of a patient with height phobia. This patient was treated by exposure to a virtual lift that travelled many floors; eventually the patient was exposed to a virtual precipice! It is easy to see how this method might be extremely helpful for patients with phobias of flying or in treating patients in a preparatory way before they embark on their trip on the underground or to a busy shopping centre.

The major advantages of this treatment are that the therapist will probably need to go out of the clinic much less, and virtual reality environments are surely going to become much more accessible to the general population. Furthermore, the equipment required is likely to become increasingly available in the near future as its use increase and patients can plan to do their treatment 'homework' exercises at a time and a place to suit themselves rather than the therapist or indeed anyone else.

Conclusion

As this chapter has shown three main approaches are used to treat anxiety disorders. The main question for the sufferer must be 'What is the evidence regarding the efficacy of each of these approaches?'. The answer is fairly straightforward; there is very little evidence to support the widespread use of the traditional psychotherapeutic treatments, including counselling. However, there are individuals who do benefit from such approaches although it is very difficult to determine to determine exactly who these people are likely to be. Psychotherapeutic treatments usually take considerable time and, perhaps, the most sensible suggestion is that they should be held in reserve if the other two approaches fail.

The evidence to support the effectiveness of drug therapy is stronger than that of psychotherapy and the newer antidepressants seem to offer the most hope for sufferers. There is no doubt that drug treatments will be refined in future and, as I have indicated in the chapter on causation, advances in genetics may well yield a real breakthrough. In the first instance this may be in the form of a specific medication. However, that day is a long way off.

There is no doubt that the behavioural and cognitive behavioural treatments have the greatest amount of evidence to support their use as the first line method of treatment. The central element of this approach is exposure therapy. However, this form of treatment is by no means a panacea and a great deal more work needs to be done on refining treatment approaches. Furthermore, access to a suitably qualified therapist is important; this will be covered in the next chapter.

There is no doubt that professionals who may offer some help and assistance for sufferers are available in every health district of the UK. The nature of that help may, however, vary. As a result, your first question must always be to ask what help is likely to be available in your area and who is going to give it? Sometimes that help may be an inappropriate drug or a 'talking treatment' that has no evidence to support it. It is, therefore, extremely important that sufferers should know who the professionals are and what their qualifications mean. Patients should also always be informed about the nature of, and the evidence for, the treatments they are offered. If this information is not made available to you, do not be afraid to ask for it.

My guiding principle is that the National Health Service belongs to all of us and is funded by every one of us in one way or another. Thus the professionals working within it must not put themselves on a pedestal and every professional should be obliged to answer direct questions about the validity of the treatment approaches that they offer. Unfortunately some professionals are guilty of arrogance about their practice and, again unfortunately, patients may then perceive that they have been viewed with contempt by the doctors and the therapists whose job is to provide a service designed to help them.

Who then is qualified to treat phobias and/or panic disorders?

A professional qualification does not, in itself, equip the person with expertise in treating anxiety. Conversely, a GP who has never received any particular training may have learned to apply common-sense principles to the management of anxiety and phobias and may do an excellent job. Generally speaking, however, there are three large groups of professionals who may be able to offer appropriate specialist treatment for panic and phobias.

First, psychiatrists are medically qualified doctors who have received specialist training in the management of mental health problems. Some psychiatrists may have taken a special interest in anxiety and phobic states while all should have received training that allows them to discriminate between effective and non-effective treatments. Thus, psychiatrists should generally be able to offer a range of skills that are valuable in the treatment of phobias, panic and anxiety. In addition, a small number of psychiatrists in the UK have undergone further training that allows them to treat these states by behavioural and cognitive behavioural methods. Most such psychiatrists work in large cities, teaching hospitals or research centres so that their skills are not freely available to the more widespread population.

The second group with specific expertise in this area are clinical psychologists, not all of whom will have received specialist training in behavioural or cognitive behavioural treatments. However, training courses in clinical psychology increasingly require that psychologists have treated a number of people by this method by the time they qualify.

Clinical psychologists with cognitive behavioural expertise are now much more widely available over the country although there may be long waiting lists, perhaps several months, for treatment. In some areas, referral to a psychologist can be made directly by a GP but, in others, referral is only possible by a consultant psychiatrist who, in turn, will have needed to receive a referral from the patient's GP.

Nurse therapists, trained psychiatric nurses who have received a very intensive training in behaviour therapy and cognitive behaviour therapy, are also available in some parts of the country and have specific expertise in treating phobias, panics and anxiety states This programme was established by Isaac Marks at the Maudsley Hospital nearly a quarter of a century ago and, since then, several hundred nurse therapists have been trained.

There are currently about 200 trained nurse therapists in the UK employed by various mental health services. This training has been very widely researched and the evidence shows that these therapists achieve results that are as good, if not better, than those achieved by clinical psychologists or psychiatrists. However, because of the expense of the training programme, and the fact that there are only a handful of specialist behaviour therapy centres in the UK, the number of nurse therapists is woefully inadequate to service the number of people with anxiety states. More than 10 years ago Isaac Marks estimated that we needed not 200 but 2,000 nurse therapists in the UK to provide an adequate service to people with phobias and obsessions.

It can be seen, therefore, that only a few professionals have been specially trained to treat phobias and anxiety states by behavioural and cognitive behavioural methods. These small numbers may be augmented by a small number of social workers and occupational therapists who have received specialist training in behaviour therapy but these probably number but a few dozen.

Who is suitably qualified and experienced?

As stated above, a GP is the main source of referral for specialist treatment. However, I would strongly advise that prospective patients are fully informed about the qualifications and background of the person who is to see them.

All psychiatrists are medically qualified and, therefore, have a code of conduct and a professional body that protects both the patient and the doctor. Likewise, psychologists in the Health Service will hold certain minimum qualifications. Although it is likely that all psychologists will have to register in the next few years it is, at present, not necessary for them to be registered with the British Psychological Society as a Chartered Psychologist. Despite this, the vast majority of psychologists will be listed in The Register of Chartered Psychologists that should be available in any public library.

Accreditation by the British Association for Cognitive and Behavioural Psychotherapy means that your therapist will have attained certain minimal standards and you can, therefore, be sure that they have received specialist training in this form of treatment and that their practice is regularly monitored by an appropriately qualified supervisor. All accredited psychotherapists are also registered with the United Kingdom Council for Psychotherapy. However, this registration alone does not necessarily mean that the person will have expertise in the treatment of anxiety states; it merely means that they have achieved certain minimum standards as a psychotherapist. The register for the United Kingdom Council for Psychotherapy is available in any public library.

What does all this mean for the sufferer? If you are being referred for behavioural or cognitive behavioural treatment (including exposure therapy) you should be prepared to ask your therapist if they are accredited. Checking whether someone is appropriately qualified and experienced only provides you with an assurance that the treatment that you are to receive will be of a high standard. You should apply the same rules to seeking the services of a therapist as to seeking a garage that is likely to give your car a good service! Unfortunately, first impressions may be misleading and, at the end of the day, perhaps the best reassurance may come from a GP who has had experience of a very large number of patients treated by that person.

At this point I think it is worth mentioning the bewildering array of alternative and complementary therapists who treat patients with anxiety disorders using techniques as diverse as acupuncture, aromatherapy, reflexology and hypnosis. Unfortunately for the sufferer many of these therapists have no real qualifications in medical or psychological care although their advertisements may show an impressive number of letters after their name.

Although there is no doubt that some individuals may benefit from some of these approaches it is, from my point of view, difficult to urge anything other than scepticism and extreme caution as I know of no properly controlled research evidence that testifies to the effectiveness of any of these procedures. Furthermore, I am painfully aware that many patients I have seen have wasted huge amounts of time and money pursuing help for these conditions from those providing alternative methods of treatment.

Methods of Referral

As mentioned above, the main agent of referral for specialist help within the National Health Service is the General Practitioner. GPs in general are now much more aware of mental health problems and are increasingly sympathetic to those seeking specialist treatment for their problems. However, there are some unsympathetic GPs who are simply ignorant of the significant distress that may be caused by phobias, anxiety and panic or, indeed, of the routes of referral to appropriate specialists. In such cases, it does pay to be assertive and, even if resources are not available in your home area, the new funding arrangements in the National Health Service make it possible for your GP to apply for what is known as an 'extra contractual referral' (ECR). This enables the patient to receive treatment appropriate to their condition from an appropriately qualified specialist regardless of where that person lives.

Specialist services, such as those offered by the Maudsley Hospital in London, have always taken referrals from around the country. ECR now gives people greater opportunity to receive treatment at centres of excellence and is now the only route for funding treatment under the NHS outside one's immediate health area.

Those with private health insurance can obtain private care and there are now a number of private hospitals that offer treatment for anxiety disorders. However, most insurance companies have a limit to the extent of coverage they will provide so that some patients will not be able to access adequate private treatment even though they are covered by a health insurance. Such companies may either limit the amount of treatment or, in many cases, will not provide any cover for certain mental health problems. This means that patients with private medical insurance should always make exhaustive inquiries of their insurers before they embark on a course of private treatment as this may prove to be very expensive. For example, a private psychiatric assessment in Inner London may cost up to £150 per visit and therapy is often charged at between £60 and £140 per hour depending on the expertise of the therapist. The bill for the treatment of a relatively non-serious problem may, therefore, run into several thousands of pounds.

Conclusion

Sufferers of anxiety states should be aware that they have a right to treatment by a properly qualified therapist within the National Health Service. Treatment is normally provided by a psychiatrist, psychologist or a nurse therapist. My advice is to stick to orthodox routes of referral and your GP must, wherever possible, be the central pivot for your health care. Sufferers should not be afraid to check the qualifications and experience of the people they consult and I would urge extreme caution if you feel that they deviate from traditional routes of referral.

However, sufferers should feel a great deal of confidence in the main self-help organisations in the UK and be aware that *No Panic*, and *Triumph over Phobia* both have a very active group of highly qualified and experienced professionals to advise them on their work.

The last piece of simple advice is, therefore, that if you are not sure about how to seek referral, or if you require advice about how to check whether the therapist you are seeing is properly qualified, you should ask for advice from the telephone help lines listed at the back of this book. I can certainly vouch for the fact that, *No Panic*, the self-help organisation with which I am associated, will always be able to provide sound and sensible information. If the person at the end of the telephone does not have an immediate answer they will be able to obtain information for you.

SECTION 2: INTRODUCTION TO SELF-HELP

Approaches to self-help

Most of the text books and journal articles that discuss anxiety disorders concern themselves with professional approaches to treatment which, as we have seen, range from various types of psychotherapy to a variety of drug treatments. Unfortunately there has been little emphasis on self-help methods although a number of researchers across the world have now shown that such approaches can, in many situations, be as effective as professional treatment.

There is absolutely no reason why patients should not use the principles of self-help. Provided that sufferers receive some form of guidance through self-help books, coupled with encouragement from those around them, there is no reason why they should not be able to make major gains. In addition, there are now a number of self-help organisations around the country, notably *Triumph over Phobia* and *No Panic*, which offer not just a listening ear but also down-to-earth and practical advice based on the interventions that have been used by professionals.

Obviously, if you choose to try self-help methods you should give them a reasonable chance of working but, if after applying the principles consistently and systematically, you are not really benefiting and making progress in managing your problem, you should return to your GP and seek possible referral to a specialist.

Steps in a self-help programme

There are certain steps that should be followed in any treatment programme whether this is managed by a professional or by a self-treatment method. They are:

- Defining your problem
- Selecting targets or goals
- Deciding on, and implementing, a plan for intervention and defining factors that will make that intervention more effective (e.g. enlisting help from a partner or friend)
- Managing panic and general anxiety using other strategies that will reduce background anxiety and stress (e.g. by attending to exercise, diet, alcohol consumption relaxation and time management).

This section explores various approaches that may be taken in attempts to treat the conditions by helping yourself.

CHAPTER 5:   DEFINING YOUR PROBLEM

Although it may seem rather obvious, defining the precise nature of your problem is the first step on the road to recovery. It is essential to define exactly what the problem is in clear and unambiguous terms. For example, saying 'simply' that you are agoraphobic or that you are a panicker does not really clarify *exactly* what it is that makes life so difficult.

If we take the example of agoraphobia, we can see just how much there is to the problem. The term generally indicates that the sufferer has a number of fears that, in turn, may concern particular situations. Furthermore, these are usually accompanied by certain thoughts, such as *'I'm going to pass out'*, *'I'm going to collapse'* or *'I must escape'*. There may also be factors that make the problem better or worse. For example, using a walking stick may help someone with a fear of fainting or carrying a Valium tablet in a bottle in your pocket may make provide security enabling you to feel that you have something 'to fall back on' if 'the worst comes to the worst'.

Alternatively, situations may be made worse by certain things. For example, the very bright lights in a supermarket may worsen feelings of unreality and sufferers may feel 'strange'; some patients have much greater problems at certain times in their menstrual cycle for example while others may feel worse at night and so on. It is, therefore, worth exploring your problem in some depth so that you can see exactly what it is you are fighting in clear detail. Some examples of how you might define an agoraphobic fear are as follows:

1. Fear of situations where there is no obvious escape (e.g. crowded buses, trains and tubes). This fear leads

to an avoidance of the situation which, in turn, restricts ability to work and to socialise.

2. The fear may comprise thoughts connected with a loss of control (e.g. passing out, fainting, collapsing, becoming incontinent). Although these thoughts may be recognised as irrational, exposure to the situation may make them seem overwhelming to the point where the sufferer feels that these fears are about to come to fruition.

The consistent avoidance of situations provoking such fears may lead to problems of self-esteem and pessimism. Sufferers may compare themselves unfavourably with others and feel that the future has nothing to offer. In general, therefore, they may feel that they are a failure; this then inhibits them from undertaking new hobbies, looking for a job, etc. Eventually despair and depression may result.

It may be helpful to break down the problem in slightly different ways. What is important is that, before you start, you define the list of things that are causing you difficulty and, within this list:

a. Try to isolate exactly what it is that you are afraid of happening (e.g. collapsing, dying, fainting)

b. Define the situations that are the source of anxiety (i.e. when and where does it occur?)

c. Define how the avoidance of these situations leads to handicap (i.e. what effects does it have on you?).

It is also worth trying to identify what makes a situation better or worse. For example, a person with a fear of collapsing in the supermarket may find that wheeling a trolley, or even carrying a walking-stick, may be helpful because of the feeling of security it gives them.

The reason why these modifying factors are so important is that they can be used in treatment. Thus, if there are three or four things that make a situation better, you should gradually practise doing without these things - not all at once, but one at a time.

As I shall point out below, the plan for exposure to those situations that normally cause you difficulty should be well thought through with the emphasis on gradually increasing exposure. Similarly, graduating the approach towards reducing the reliance on modifying factors is also essential.

Summary

To summarise, defining your problem is the first step on the road to recovery. Make sure that you do the following:

- Think about all of the components that make up your problem
- Identify those situations which cause you difficulty or which you tend to avoid
- Define the thoughts which trouble you
- Identify all those factors which make the problem worse or better
- Define how the problem upsets and/or interferes with your normal activities.

Once you have done this you can then begin to go on to the next stage which is to select your treatment targets or goals.

CHAPTER 6:   SELECTING TARGETS OR GOALS

The very first question you should ask yourself is: *'What would I like to do that I can't do at present because of my problems?'*. This is important and should be answered honestly, bearing in mind that other people might, sometimes, want you to do things that you do not necessarily want to do for yourself! It is the effects that your problems have on you that are important here.

Target setting should be a two-stage process. First you must decide what goals (targets) you wish to achieve and then you should define each of these in detail.

Initial Targets

Returning to your original list of problems should help you to see what targets can be developed. For example, if your fear is of shopping centres, the target might simply be to go shopping with a friend twice a week. If your fear is of underground trains, the target might be to travel to work using the tube. If your problem concerns panic, your target might be to face up to panicky feelings when they occur and to prevent yourself avoiding or escaping by concentrating on strategies designed to reduce or eliminate your symptoms.

If your problem stops you doing things that you enjoy, such as pursuing your hobbies or interests, you should begin by trying to develop targets that are enjoyable in their own right but which may involve exposure to situations that would normally cause anxiety. Joining an evening class or a gym are obvious examples.

Detailing your targets

Like problem statements, targets need to be specific. This is illustrated by the following example. Let us start from the point of saying that one of your targets might be to travel by bus. This does not, in itself, tell you very much about the precise behaviour you are aiming for, and does not focus on the different aspects of the problem that must be tackled. A suitable target might be:

> 'To travel by bus from my house to the town centre at least three times a week in the rush hour. Furthermore, this journey should be undertaken alone, and without the aid of the tranquilliser that I normally take before such journeys.'

Obviously you may wish to develop target behaviours in a more gradual way so that your first target might be:

> 'To travel by bus from my house to the town centre at 11.00am, with a friend, and to return before the busy period starts, and to do this at least twice a week.'

Similarly, if your problem concerns shopping, your eventual aim might be:

> 'To shop at least once a week for at least ninety minutes in a busy supermarket (on a Friday evening or Saturday morning), and to practise waiting in the longest queue.'

However, an intermediate target might be to spend thirty minutes in the same supermarket, twice a week in quiet periods accompanied by a friend or family member.

Ideally, each problem statement should have at least three goal (or target) statements attached to it. It does not matter how many targets you set but it is worth considering how these can be broken down so that you can tackle them in stages. For example, you may choose to set goals in the short-term (i.e. within four weeks), medium-term (i.e. within three months) and longer-term (i.e. within six months to one year).

Your targets should, therefore, be arranged in a list. Remember you should go through the following stages:

- Make a list of the things you wish to do
- Be very specific about the detail of each target
- Make sure that the target meets with your problem statement
- Think about your targets in the short-, medium- and long-term. Don't be afraid to revise your targets and think about them again. This should be the whole basis for your programme and the plan of action that will be discussed in Chapter 7.

When you have made this list, you should then discuss this with your spouse, partner or friend to see whether there are additional items you should add and to seek their support in achieving your goals. When target setting is complete you should date your list and keep referring to it to check that you are on course.

CHAPTER 7: DECIDING ON, AND IMPLEMENTING, A PLAN FOR INTERVENTION

A central theme throughout this book, and indeed of all good self-help texts, is that exposure to the object or situation that causes anxiety is essential if you are to overcome your fears. If this is to be achieved the central element of your plan *must* include exposure. However, other aspects of anxiety management and anxiety control are also important [for example attention to exercise, diet and sleep should also be included in your plan (see Chapter 9)].

In drawing up your plan, it is usually helpful to write down all of the aspects of that plan that you can think of and to consider these in the light of any constraints imposed by your normal routine or your list of life priorities. In my experience, if one is to overcome a phobia, this needs to be done as a maximum priority. Making the decision to act is the key element. If you cannot decide that the plan is your number one priority you will probably not succeed in overcoming your fears.

Drawing up your plan

Three central issues must be addressed:

1. Planning exposure to your feared object or situation
2. How you will manage panic if it arises
and 3. The general management of anxiety and stress.

First, if you have a phobic anxiety state, there is absolutely no doubt that you must plan to increase your exposure to your feared object or situation. I make no apologies for repeating this message over and again. Sufferers *must* accept that recovery from their problem will involve facing up to that which makes them afraid. The main principles of this approach are explored below.

The second element is deciding how you will manage panic if it occurs, whether this be a general phenomenon or part of the phobic fear. There is, of course, great overlap between exposure and panic management and, for most practical purposes, the two cannot really be separated.

The third element concerns the general management of anxiety and stress. Some of this material is included in my book on Stress Management (Gournay, 1995) but I think it is essential that sufferers from panic and phobias consider these topics.

Generally speaking, panic and phobias are made much worse when general stress levels are high. Four particular aspects of this problem have been selected for discussion here (i.e. exercise, alcohol, diet and time management). Some relaxation training may be helpful and, although relaxation will not, in itself, make any difference to your phobia, it may help reduce your general level of arousal so that you will feel less tense. The feeling of well-being will, in turn, help you fight your problem more effectively. Simple relaxation exercises are suggested in Chapter 9.

Planning your exposure

In order to benefit from self-help it is important to understand the details of the treatment method. Thus, the most helpful way of planning your treatment is to consider how exposure can be used most effectively to help you to overcome your difficulties. In describing the possible approaches I have drawn on the considerable research that has been carried out world-wide with consistent findings.

Exposure in real life or exposure in imagination

The early treatment methods of the 1950s and 1960s relied on the patient's imagination. Simply, patients were taught to imagine their feared situation and then taught to relax during this process. Over the years, exposure in imagination became redundant and therapists emphasised the need to face up to one's fears in 'real life'. However, there is now ample evidence that imaginal exposure can be very helpful in the early stages of treatment.

In simple terms, try to visualise (imagine) yourself in the situation or facing the feared object while, at the same time, trying to imagine yourself staying there and coping with that situation. This can be a very helpful preparation for the 'real thing'.

Most phobics will have thoughts about the situation although they usually try to push these out of their consciousness and so, do not think about the situation for very long. Imaginal exposure requires that they think about the situation or object for longer periods (i.e. at least 10 minutes at a time) if this approach is to be successful.

How often/how long?

Research shows very clearly that long sessions of exposure are much more effective than short sessions. This can be explained by thinking about what happens when you actually face up to your feared situation. In practice you will begin to calm down after a few minutes. Lasting anxiety reduction, however, often takes much longer and the longer you stay in the situation the better, because your body can only keep up high levels of adrenaline output for relatively brief periods. In addition, the longer your exposure the more you will realise that your central fears will not come to fruition.

Ideally, exposure sessions should last two hours and, although this sounds like a tall order, there is a great deal of evidence to show that this length of exposure is much more effective in the longer term than shorter periods of 30 minutes or so. Although there is no firm guidance about how often your sessions should take place, regular practice is important. The simple rule of thumb is that, if at all possible, you should try and face your fears on a daily basis. My experience is that doing as much as you can will always be more helpful than being conservative. I believe that there is very little risk from frequent sessions and that, although many people anticipate that they may 'overdo it', this is probably not so.

How gradual should your exposure be?

Some people can progress very quickly to facing their most feared situation, others may take a little longer. Thus, for example, some phobics can very quickly graduate to doing the worst thing that they can imagine (for example, travelling on a crowded underground train in the rush hour) while others need to approach their fears very gradually. Research does not really reveal any conclusive evidence, and one should be guided by the simple principle that you should push yourself to do what is difficult but just about manageable.

Do you need to suffer anxiety at exposure sessions?

Although most phobics dread exposure treatment, and anticipate very high levels of anxiety, the amount of anxiety experienced when actually confronting the feared situation or object is very variable. Indeed, a significant minority of patients suffer very little anxiety when they eventually face up to a situation that they may have avoided for many years. In this case, some people worry that they are not anxious enough! The simple answer is that it does not seem to matter how much anxiety people suffer during an exposure session, provided that they continue to practise systematically since this will gradually help them to overcome their fear.

Going it alone or working with another phobic

Some research shows that group treatments can be very effective in treating phobia and panic in some individuals. The reason for this is probably that working with others often provides additional confidence, motivation and reinforcement. Many of the treatment programmes I have run in hospital out-patient settings have involved group approaches, and the camaraderie that develops is very often very positive. Furthermore, many patients keep in touch with each other between sessions and after treatment and encourage each other through set-backs as well as successes.

Nevertheless, group treatment is not for everybody, and some people are positively put off by working with others. If you are a member of a self-help group, you may be offered a group approach. *No Panic*, for example, uses a telephone conference system, whereby sufferers 'meet' once a week on the telephone. The purposes of such groups are to set each other targets and provide encouragement and support. Again, this is not for everyone, and some people genuinely want to go it alone.

My advice is that, if a group approach is offered, you should try it because, on balance, the strengths of this approach in tackling your problem may outweigh its disadvantages and it may be easier than trying to do this unsupported by other sufferers. However, in the final analysis, it is up to you!

You must remember that, although you should take as much practical help as possible from others, your ultimate goal is to face situations alone. You should, therefore, always be aware that having someone with you is an intermediate strategy only. Many sufferers are all too painfully aware that excessive dependence on others may eventually be detrimental.

Do you *need* a professional therapist?

The straightforward answer to this question is generally 'No'. Provided that you can follow the central principles, and that those around you are supportive, self-exposure may be as good as receiving help from a professional therapist. However, professional therapists can provide an objective assessment of your problem, and may help by providing you with the encouragement you need to face the situation or object.

Many years ago, therapists like myself spent sometimes literally hundreds of hours with patients helping them to face their feared situations. Thus I have spent many hours on tubes, trains and shopping centres, coaxing and encouraging phobics to face up to their fears. Although there were some excellent results with this approach, there are drawbacks. For example, the patient can become overly reliant on the therapist, and many hours of therapist-aided exposure may merely be a way of putting off the inevitable time when the patient has to face their fears alone. As a rule of thumb, I would say that if therapist-aided exposure is indicated, this should be to introduce the person to the situation, after which therapist should fade into the background. Unless there are exceptional reasons, six sessions of therapist assistance should be the maximum.

Using a co-therapist

Facing any problem always proves more successful if you have the help and encouragement of those around you. It therefore makes absolute sense to enlist the aid of a co-therapist. However, a co-therapist needs to know what to do and when to do it.

Most people with phobias and panics receive considerable help from others but, unless this is carefully thought through, such help can, at times, be counter-productive. For example, the husband of someone with agoraphobia may take over a number of responsibilities that the person would normally undertake for themselves. In the end, this shift of responsibility can be detrimental and will promote an increased dependency on others. The spouse or partner may also get drawn into giving endless and meaningless reassurance and, eventually, reassurance-seeking may become the main point of interaction. The spouse or partner may also become an extra source of security, being with the sufferer day and night and having to accompany them whenever a feared situation must be faced.

If you choose to enlist the help of a co-therapist, this person should recognise that their previous behaviour may have been counter-productive. It is not always easy to break old habits so that the treatment plan may have to involve the co-therapist gradually changing their behaviour as well. Co-therapists should read books such as this thoroughly and be totally involved with the planning of the programme. That is not to say that they should take over the running of the programme as this will, of course, be counter-productive and just reinforce dependency.

The role of the co-therapist is to provide encouragement and assistance to help the sufferer to face up to their feared and avoided situations and, at the same time, provide on-going reinforcement. This, like many other things, is easier said than done and there will, of course, be pitfalls. If, however, the phobic person and their co-therapist review progress objectively, perhaps using the diaries described below, many of these can be avoided.

The co-therapist should initially provide assistance with entering the phobic situation or facing the phobic object but plans should be made for the gradual withdrawal of the assistance they provide.

Diary keeping

There are numerous ways in which you can keep a diary; three examples are provided below.

The first is a *General Diary* wherein day-to-day activities and ratings of your level of anxiety and mood are noted (Figure 7.1). Recording such information over a period of time will help you to see the relationship between what you do and how you feel. The 'comments' section at the end can be used to summarise your overall feelings for the day.

Figure 7.1   **Format of a general diary**

Date	Main events of the day	High/low anxiety points*	Mood ratings**	Comments

* Score anxiety on a scale from 0 - 8   0 = No anxiety
                                            8 = Worst anxiety possible

**Score depression on a scale from 0 - 8 0 = No problems
                                            8 = Worst depression possible

The second type of diary, an *Exposure Diary*, is specific to exposure tasks, and records the length of your session and your anxiety ratings (Figure 7.2). You should record your anxiety ratings before, during and after the session. It is also important to note whether a co-therapist has been present, and then to plan your next task. This simple format can be modified and extra columns added as required.

Figure 7.2   **Format of an exposure diary**

Date	Exposure situation	Length of session	Anxiety ratings*	Co-therapist present?	Next task planned

* Score anxiety on a scale   0 = No anxiety/panic
   from 0 - 8   8 = Worst possible anxiety or panic

The *Thoughts Diary* (Figure 7.3) may be particularly valuable for panic sufferers and will help you identify various patterns of negative and catastrophic thoughts.

This is an important process that acts as a first step in managing the thoughts associated with panic attacks. Various strategies will be described in the next chapter.

Figure 7.3 **General format of a thoughts diary**

Date	Situation	Triggers	Thoughts	Consequences

Overall, diaries of how you feel, what you do and how successful you are provide perhaps the best ways of evaluating your progress. You should keep your original list of problems and targets and use the diaries as a way of determining how close you are to achieving the targets you have set for yourself.

It may well be that, after a while, your targets need revising and, indeed, it may become clear as you go on that your view of your problems changes so that you need to revise your original definition. This often happens when you have avoided something for a long time and it is not until you begin to face things that you begin to see things in a different light.

CHAPTER 8:   DEALING WITH SPECIFIC PHOBIAS

The same rules of exposure apply to managing specific phobias as to the more complex phobias such as agoraphobia. However, the approach needs to be specifically tailored to both the phobia in question and to the individual circumstances. It may be helpful to describe the treatment of a patient with a bird phobia to illustrate how self-treatment can work.

Liz has suffered from a phobia of pigeons for as long as she can remember. She can recall several occasions as a child when her phobia prevented her from going on school journeys and she remembers being unable to go to the National Gallery in London because of its situation on the edge of Trafalgar Square. Birds other than pigeons also made her feel uncomfortable but pigeons, in particular, caused her to feel very panicky, and she sometimes had nightmares about pigeons flying into her face. She remembers seeing the Hitchcock movie, The Birds, and having to leave after about fifteen minutes. On some occasions, she came across groups of pigeons and, in her words, became 'hysterical'. When she left school she did not need to visit places with pigeons as she worked in a quiet suburban office.

Her problem came to the fore when she started to go out with a young man who was an avid football fan. She accompanied him to a match for the first time and was horrified to find flocks of pigeons near the entrance to the ground. Although she managed to keep herself under control she found that the whole experience of the match was overwhelmed by her vision of the flock of pigeons before the match and a terror that she would encounter them when the match ended. She did not tell her boyfriend what the problem was so that he thought that he had done something to offend her! The following week, her boyfriend suggested they went to London to see a film, and Liz happily agreed. However, they arrived early, and to her horror, he suggested that they went to the National Gallery. At this point she broke down and told him of her phobia and, shortly afterwards, she decided to seek treatment.

Following a thorough assessment, the therapist decided that Liz was a suitable candidate for self-treatment. After some considerable discussion, Liz and her therapist agreed that she should do a number of things to prepare herself for facing pigeons in 'real life' and Liz realised that, if she was to overcome her fear, she would need, eventually, to make a trip to Trafalgar Square. The very thought of doing this filled her with horror; even talking about it made her heart beat faster and she broke into a sweat. She set herself a number of exercises directed towards helping her begin the process of exposure.

First, she joined the Royal Society for the Protection of Birds and along with her first subscription came a number of magazines filled with pictures. She then managed to obtain some copies of videos of birds and, after visiting several toy shops, she found a cardboard cut-out of a pigeon that she suspended over her bed. She then spent the next three weeks looking at pictures and watching videos and, every morning, she woke up to see a cardboard pigeon swinging from the ceiling!

At this point she embarked on trying to find pigeons that she could observe from a distance and found a local shopping centre where pigeons tended to congregate. She thus positioned herself twenty yards away and made herself watch the pigeons for twenty to twenty-five minutes at a time.

Following these exercises, her next exposure task was to visit the Snowdon Aviary at London Zoo. Although she coincidentally saw a few pigeons from a distance her main task here was to expose herself to other birds that, prior to her treatment, had made her feel uncomfortable. However she felt that she could begin to face up to the birds in the Aviary as a method of preparing herself.

After meeting with her therapist again to review progress, it was agreed that Liz should try to imagine herself in Trafalgar Square with a group of pigeons, and to keep this image in her mind for as long as possible. The therapist instructed her that she should try and imagine herself coping with the experience and to try to visualise spreading some bread crumbs for the birds. At the same time, she agreed to keep the other exposure exercises going. Although she found that these self-treatment exercises consumed a great deal of her time, Liz had begun to feel better about facing pigeons and her trips to the shopping centre evoked much less anxiety.

Some six weeks after her first assessment, and following only two brief sessions with the therapist, Liz spontaneously decided that she should enlist the help of her boyfriend and take a trip to Charing Cross Station and walk as close as she could to Trafalgar Square to observe the flocks of pigeons at a distance. She managed to stand on the other side of the road, away from the main square, for half an hour in the company of her boyfriend, and her anxiety level dropped from her initial high rating of 7 to 4 (out of 8). (Liz's therapist had instructed her on the use of the Anxiety Rating shown on page 62).

After this session, Liz was very pleased with her progress and telephoned her therapist, who suggested that she should repeat the exercise and that, this time, she should try and make it to the edge of the square itself. She did this successfully, and surprised herself by feeling calm enough after fifteen minutes to take a few tentative steps on her own into the Square at which point a pigeon flew very close to her head, and she panicked. Nevertheless, having previously discussed the possibility of an incident such as this with her therapist, she took a few minutes to compose herself, and set off once more into the Square.

After yet another phone call to her therapist, Liz repeated the exposure exercise and, after four more trips, found herself being able to take the final step of feeding the pigeons who gathered at her feet. Six months after her treatment finished, Liz visited her therapist for a review. Liz agreed that she was now able to go about her daily life without being pre-occupied with birds and she had in fact made two or three trips to the National Gallery with her boyfriend. She was, however, still slightly anxious when she saw a pigeon or a group of pigeons in the street but now felt that she was over her problem.

This case history illustrates the step-by-step approach to exposure, and shows how a problem can be broken down into difficult but manageable steps. In Liz's case, her therapist really only needed to see her for one long session of assessment, taking about an hour and a half; subsequent therapy, including telephone conversations, then required approximately another hour and a half.

In some cases of specific phobia, however, the therapist may need to help the patient introduce themselves to the phobic situation; other patients may, however, need even less therapist assistance than Liz. The point is that you must be prepared to face your fear and let the anxiety fade away.

CHAPTER 9:   MANAGING PANIC AND GENERAL ANXIETY

Panic management essentially comprises three central approaches. The first, and perhaps the most important, is to maintain exposure and to prevent yourself 'escaping' from the situation. The other two main elements are dealing with over-breathing and hyperventilation and dealing with catastrophic thoughts.

Over-breathing and hyperventilation

When we become anxious our whole reaction is, essentially, one of 'fight or flight' as the body prepares for activity. One element of this reaction is an increase in respiration that will provide the body with the additional oxygen it requires. However, in anxiety and panic, the increase in respiration is not required to help us to fight or fly and we are, in effect, breathing in excess of our bodily requirements.

Over time this will lead to an imbalance in body chemistry and an associated reduction in carbon dioxide levels which, in turn, changes the acid-alkali balance of the blood. The consequence of these changes is that sensations, such as pins-and-needles, feeling light-headed, yawning or sighing are experienced and, in extreme cases, muscle spasms develop. Long-lasting over-breathing also causes fatigue and sleepiness. Sufferers of panic often find these symptoms frightening in themselves and, taken with other symptoms of anxiety - such as a rapid heart rate, they may feel that they are just about to have a stroke or a heart attack. As a result, the body produces more adrenaline; this, in turn, increases the vicious circle of anxiety.

There is considerable evidence to show that teaching people to breathe more appropriately can be very effective in helping to reduce hyperventilation. The difficulty for some sufferers is that panic develops so abruptly that they do not realise that they are hyperventilating.

Dealing with hyperventilation

Although respiration is increased, hyperventilation usually leads to breathing being restricted to the upper part of the chest. Simple breathing exercises, consisting of taking slow but not too deep breaths, can be extremely helpful. Ensure that your breathing is from the diaphragm rather than from the top of the chest. You can check that you are achieving this by placing your hand on your abdomen, slightly below the rib-cage, to ensure that as much of the chest as possible is used.

Generally speaking, sufferers from hyperventilation can reverse the pattern of over-breathing by practising slow diaphragmatic breathing once or twice a day combining this, if possible, with a period of physical relaxation. Sufferers should also try to undertake physical exercise, such as running, cycling or swimming, as a regular part of their daily programme.

What to do in the case of acute panic

If possible one should try to attempt to either sit or lie down in a quiet place and try to take slow breaths from the diaphragm; it is helpful to loosen your clothing and relax your posture. Although this can be very difficult, try to concentrate on physical relaxation and, at the same time, remember that panic can do no real harm.

One very rapid and effective way of dealing with the hyper-ventilation associated with panic is the old tried and tested method of re-breathing expired air. Expired air contains more carbon dioxide than the air around us, and re-breathing it replenishes carbon dioxide thus reversing the chemical changes that follow from hyper-ventilation. You can re-breathe expired air by breathing in and out of a paper bag but, if this is not possible, a simple alternative is to cup your hands over your nose and mouth and re-breathe the expired air in this way. Doing this for two or three minutes is generally enough to restore the correct chemical balance in the body.

If you are in the company of someone who hyperventilates, one of the key principles in managing the problem is to remain calm yourself. It is important to remember that hyperventilation is usually self-limiting and rarely has any permanent medical consequences; very occasionally it can lead to muscular spasm although this, in itself, is also harmless and self-limiting and is the body's way of stopping over-breathing until the chemical balance is restored. Stay with the person, and try to ensure that they remain still; try to help them to relax and emphasise the need to breathe slowly and from the diaphragm. Use the paper bag 'trick' or encourage the sufferer to use cupped hands to re-breathe expired air.

Dealing with Catastrophic Thoughts

If you keep a record of your panic attacks, perhaps using a diary as previously described (pages 62-64), you will find that the thoughts accompanying such attacks will be much the same. For most sufferers the central theme tends to be fear of some sort of loss of control. This may amount to fainting, having a stroke, having a heart attack or dying.

One of the most important ways of dealing with such catastrophic thoughts is to examine the 'evidence'. For example, you may have panicked on numerous occasions but when did this lead to anything other than anxiety? Did you have a heart attack? Did you faint?

Remember that panic is harmless and self-limiting and that other people are usually completely unaware that anything is happening.

It is likely that, in the long run, escaping will make the panic worse. What you should attempt to do is to stay in the situation, breathe slowly, and repeat to yourself that nothing will happen. Recall your past experience - although you may have thought that a heart attack or stroke was imminent this has never happened. Remember also that the body can only pump out adrenaline for brief periods of time.

General Anxiety Management

For sufferers from phobias and panic, there are five important areas that are worth concentrating on in attempts to manage anxiety. These are: exercise, relaxation, alcohol, diet and time management.

Exercise

There is considerable evidence to show that regular and sensible exercise reduces the risk of coronary heart disease, hypertension and possibly some sorts of cancer; it is also clear that people who exercise regularly report lower levels of anxiety, tension and depression. Is this because exercise reduces stress or is it simply that people who lead less stressful lives have more time to exercise? The answer to this seems clear. Research clearly suggests that, regardless of background or lifestyle, regular moderate exercise not only increases cardiovascular fitness but also reduces levels of anxiety and depression.

The important thing to emphasise here is that it is *moderate* exercise that produces these results; lower-level exercise, such as playing golf or even taking a very long walk, does not have the same significant effect. A round of golf or an hour's walk may indeed produce a sense of well-being because of its distracting nature, but there is little doubt that the deeper and longer-lasting effects accruing from more strenuous exercise do not happen at this level.

Of course, those under stress often argue that they have no time for exercise and, indeed, if they took the time to go for a swim their level of stress would increase! This is a false argument as it is likely that regular exercise would increase their sense of well-being and reduce anxiety so increasing their powers of concentration and, therefore, their efficiency. Thus, in the long-term, taking time out to exercise regularly may be actually cost-efficient. It is also a matter of priority because there is clearly no contest between achieving the heights of business success and dying at the age of 45 compared with, perhaps, being marginally less committed but nevertheless successful and leading an active life well into one's middle or later years.

How much exercise should one take?

The key principle of all exercise programmes is that of graduation. If you have not exercised for a long time it is obviously wise to start slowly. Although it is generally advised that medical advice is sought before commencing an exercise programme, unless one is vastly obese or has a serious medical problem, there seems little reason why this is necessary as long as the programme begins gradually and sensibly.

For example, alternately jogging and walking for a period of ten minutes twice a week can be undertaken by anybody. You should jog until you become breathless, walk until you regain your breath and then start off again. This pattern stands more chance of success if done in company and, for those with the opportunity, a simple programme can often be planned and developed at a local sports centre for little or no cost. Here you may be able to undergo a thorough fitness assessment and be given detailed advice regarding a suitable programme.

The best exercise is found in sports, such as running, swimming, rowing or cycling, in which one attains a certain level of activity and keeps at that plateau for a reasonable period of time. The eventual aim should be to exercise at least three times a week for a minimum of twenty minutes. The rule of thumb about the level to be aimed for is to undertake the sort of activity that gets you to the point of being breathless, but just about able to say a few words.

Various formulae may be used for calculating optimum exercise levels; these generally derive from your heart rate. Heart rate monitors are now widely used by exercisers of all levels although simply taking your pulse can be just as effective. One reasonable calculation is to aim to exercise at a level that achieves about 70% of one's maximum heart rate. Maximum heart rate is generally thought to be approximately 220 minus one's age. Thus a 40-year-old should aim for exercise that gets the heart rate to about 130 beats a minute and keeps it there for a reasonable period (20 minutes or more).

One difficulty with exercise is that it is easy to become bored with doing the same thing so that longer-term strategies, designed to maintain the habit should be considered. The problems of maintaining an exercise programme are likely to occur in the first few weeks or months rather than once the habit has become firmly established. Exercising in company, joining a club, and generally varying the sports undertaken may all help to maintain your motivation.

There are, of course, some notes of caution - the principle one being that people who have very high levels of stress, and who find that exercise produces relief can, sometimes, find themselves becoming addicted to exercise itself. One does come across cases of people who end up exercising to the point of obsession so that their physical health becomes impaired. This is, of course, a problem in its own right. Despite this risk, exercise is probably the most important of all the stress management strategies and can provide a great improvement in the quality of life.

Relaxation

Although relaxation is not a direct treatment for either phobias or panic attacks, it can often be helpful in reducing the general level of physical arousal and body tension. The instructions that follow may be helpful.

Relaxation training

Relaxation training is but one way of reducing the consequences of physiological arousal. While there are many ways of achieving this, most focus on a systematic method of tensing and relaxing the muscles of the body. This has two benefits: first, it helps you to differentiate between states of tension and relaxation and, importantly, to recognise when your level of muscle tension is increasing. Second, there is considerable evidence to suggest that systematic tensing and relaxing exercises eventually lead to a state of overall muscle relaxation and a consequent feeling of well-being.

The instructions below are easy to follow. It may be helpful to read and inwardly 'digest' them and then make a tape that you can follow. If you do this, however, remember to leave a 10-second gap between each phase. This may be as effective as any commercially available tape and is certainly worth trying before investing hard-earned money!

First of all, identify a time in the day when you can spend 30 minutes to devote to this task. Find a quiet room, take the phone off the hook and wear loose, comfortable clothing. The exercises can be done in a comfortable chair or lying down and you should experiment with different situations and times of the day to clarify what the optimum conditions are for you.

Before doing the exercises, it is important to remember that when tensing your muscles, this should be done at a reasonable level since, if you tense them too hard, you will defeat the object of the exercise. A simple guide is that tensing should lead to no more than a sensation of tension or 'pulling'; if you experience pain you're trying too hard! Further, when you release the tension, this release should be immediate.

- Begin with the right hand, clench your fist and do so until your knuckles are white.

    Hold this for 5 seconds and then release immediately.

    Pause, wait 10 seconds, repeat exercise.

- Tense your forearm, close your fist and tense the muscles of your forearm. Remember not too hard.

    Hold this for 5 seconds and then release immediately.

    Pause, wait 10 seconds, repeat exercise.

- Tense your biceps, clench your fist and bend your arm to 90^0, concentrate on making your biceps muscle bulge as much as possible.

    Hold this for 5 seconds and then release immediately.

    Pause, wait 10 seconds, repeat exercise.

Repeat these actions with the left hand, forearm and biceps, remembering to do each exercise twice, hold for 10 seconds and release immediately.

- Tense your eye muscles. Screw up your eyes, hold your eyes shut tight.

  Hold this for 5 seconds and then release immediately.

  Pause, wait 10 seconds, repeat exercise.

- Tense your mouth by clenching your jaws together, concentrate on pushing your lips as firmly together as possible. At the same time you will notice that you will tense your eyes.

  Hold this for 5 seconds and then release immediately.

  Pause, wait 10 seconds, repeat exercise.

- Now concentrate on tensing your neck, push your chin down a little towards your chest but do not touch your chest with your chin.

- Push your shoulders up slightly and tense your neck. Feel the muscles tighten down into your shoulders.

  Hold this for 5 seconds and then release immediately.

  Pause, wait 10 seconds, repeat exercise.

- Tense your shoulders by pushing your arms down, holding your neck rigid. Concentrate on tensing across your shoulders.

  Hold this for 5 seconds and then release immediately.

  Pause, wait 10 seconds, repeat exercise.

- Tense the muscles in your back by pushing your elbows into your side, pushing your shoulders down, holding your neck tight, your head down towards your chest and concentrate on tensing the big muscles across your back.

Hold this for 5 seconds and then release immediately.

Pause, wait 10 seconds, repeat exercise.

- Tense the muscles of your chest by pushing your shoulders back, pushing your elbows down into your waist, tilting your head back slightly and concentrate on holding your chest in a barrel-like, rigid way.

    Hold this for 5 seconds and then release immediately.

    Pause, wait 10 seconds, repeat exercise.

- Tense the muscles of your stomach from the back and pushing towards your navel.

    Hold this for 5 seconds and then release immediately.

    Pause, wait 10 seconds, repeat exercise.

- Tense your thighs and buttocks, push your buttocks down, concentrate on tensing your thighs and buttocks together.

    Hold this for 5 seconds and then release immediately.

    Pause, wait 10 seconds, repeat exercise.

- Tense your right calf by pulling your toes up towards you, keeping your legs straight at the knee. Pull your toes back until you can feel a pull all the way up your calf muscles.

    Hold this for 5 seconds and then release immediately.

    Pause, wait 10 seconds, repeat exercise.

- Tense your right foot by curling over your toes, trying to make your toes clench like a fist.

    Hold this for 5 seconds and then release immediately.

    Pause, wait 10 seconds, repeat exercise.

Repeat this sequence for left calf and left foot.

- When you come to the end of these exercises, begin to tense your whole body, starting with your hands, working up through your arms, then head, neck, shoulders, back, chest, stomach, buttocks, thighs, calf and feet.

- Take 10 seconds to gradually tense the whole body.

    Hold for 5 seconds and relax.

- As you relax, breathe out as much as you can. Keep your eyes closed and say 'calm' to yourself.

Repeat this sequence five times remembering to leave 10 seconds between each cycle.

Now concentrate on slowing down your breathing, trying to fill all of your chest and, as you breathe out, say the word 'calm' to yourself. Let your breathing settle into a natural rhythm and then try to fix your mind on a quiet and relaxing scene. Imagine yourself lying on a beach or in a meadow. Imagine a warm atmosphere around you. Try to imagine the smells of this environment. Keep your mind as fixed as possible and let yourself drift as much as you can. Don't worry if you fall asleep but, perhaps, it may be worth setting an alarm clock!

Alcohol

Alcohol is the most widely used drug in our society and, for many, the effects are very pleasant and, indeed, beneficial. However, it is often used as an 'instant solution' to anxiety. Yet, if used to excess, alcohol can actually make anxiety worse and lead to a terrible vicious circle. Research into the use of alcohol by people with agoraphobia shows that up to one in five of them may be using alcohol at dangerously high levels and some surveys have shown that as many as one in three people admitted to alcohol treatment facilities also have a problem with phobias or panic.

You should ask yourself a number of questions about your drinking habits:

- Do I drink every day?
- Has my tolerance for alcohol changed? (Are you drinking more than before to get the same effect?)
- Has my capacity for alcohol increased or decreased?
- Do I feel guilty because of my drinking?
- Do I have memory gaps?
- Do friends comment on the amount I drink?
- Do I sometimes feel shaky after a heavy drinking session?
- Do I exceed the safe drinking limit?

There is some controversy over exactly how much represents a safe drinking limit. However, a rough guide is to say that this is between 20-30 units a week for a man and 15-20 units a week for a woman. A unit represents half a pint of beer, a pub measure of spirits, or a glass of wine Although this is an area of controversy, there is little doubt that individuals who consume greater than the amounts given above have a statistically greater chance of developing health problems or suffering social or legal consequences of their drinking (e.g. divorce and driving bans).

If you have answered 'yes' to any of the above questions, you really need to think about modifying your drinking. One of the great difficulties with answering the questions honestly is that those who have, or who may be developing, an alcohol problem often rationalise their circumstances. They may say: *'I wouldn't drink as much if my boss were nicer to me'*, *'Anyone would drink if they had my pressures'* or *'I have to drink to help me to cope with my problem or my anxiety/depression'*.

There are some important principles that you can follow which will help to ensure that your drinking remains enjoyable and without problematic consequences. They are as follows:

- Give yourself an allowance, not exceeding 21 units per week if you are a man and 14 units per week if you are a woman
- Always aim to have at least two to three days free of alcohol in any one week
- Space your drinks. Try to ensure that you never consume more than one unit per half an hour. If you are at a wedding or party that goes on for several hours do this by drinking non-alcoholic drinks in between, or dilute your wine with mineral water or your beer with lemonade
- Never drink alone
- Unless it is a social event which is out of the ordinary, never drink during the day
- Do not drink during working hours.

Try to apply these principles seriously. Use a diary to record your drinking, and do this as honestly and accurately as you can. If, after three months, you are still saying 'yes' to the questions above, you should certainly seek medical advice or go to one of the local alcohol advisory centres. In more severe cases, it may be that you need the help of Alcoholics Anonymous (the local address of AA can be found in your GP surgery, library, or telephone book; the telephone number of the Help-line is given at the end of this book).

Diet

It is not uncommon for those who suffer from panic attacks to eat badly. It is worth pointing out that a hurried eating pattern and an unbalanced diet may actually make your problem worse. Thus, for someone who is already under stress, problems can be compounded by the intake of high quantities of fat or refined sugar which leads to rapid variations in blood sugar. Indeed, we have known for many years that some people who experience panic attacks may be prone to dips in blood sugar levels (hypoglycaemia) that may, in turn, lead to further anxiety. As stated above, this may be linked to eating too many sweets and foods high in sugar.

Some people with anxiety states also hurry their meals, thus causing physical symptoms and long-term digestive problems. It is, therefore, worth considering the following advice:

- Remember to take plenty of time to enjoy your meals - try not to rush them. Allow yourself at least 30 minutes to eat a meal

- Reduce your speed of eating. Put your knife and fork down between mouthfuls, concentrating instead on chewing and enjoying the taste

- Eat plenty of carbohydrate (pasta, bread, rice and potatoes)

- Ensure that your diet contains sufficient fibre; this will help you to feel satisfied for longer. Therefore eat unrefined carbohydrate, such as wholemeal or granary bread; eat potatoes with their skins; eat beans and pulses and use dried and fresh fruit as a snack

- Avoid refined foods (e.g. sugar, white bread and fast-foods)

- Eat five portions of fresh fruit and vegetables every day

- Reduce your fat intake (grill foods rather than frying them; use skimmed rather than full fat milk and substitute low fat cheeses for full fat varieties; alternatively eat full fat cheese only once or twice a week)

- Try to eat three or four meals a day; be sure that you start with a good breakfast - fruit and cereal is good!

- Avoid snacks but, if you must, eat fruit or vegetables (dried, frozen or fresh)

- Eat with a companion if you can

- Don't eat your last meal too late at night, and try, if possible, to take a gentle walk after you have eaten.

Time Management

Many people with anxiety states feel a great pressure and urgency, and may have high levels of irritability and anger. They often seem to be attempting to do more than is realistic and are forever trying to put the proverbial 'quart into a pint pot'. This pattern obviously leads to very high levels of stress. There are several principles that you should follow to ensure that you manage your time more effectively.

1. Set yourself reasonable, and at the same time attainable, goals. Set goals for yourself in the short-, medium- and long-term but be prepared to accept that some of your goals may not be attained.
   Ensure that your goals cover all of the areas of your life, not just your work or household duties. Remember hobbies and personal interests.

2. Set daily and weekly priorities. Try to list all of the things that you want to do in the week and then

decide on the most important. Remember that we can never achieve all that we want to achieve. Be reasonable and realistic about the priorities you set for yourself.

3. Set aside a reasonable time for each activity, and allow for unexpected interruptions. Try and plan each day to work on your priorities but remember that life often throws up interruptions that are unexpected. Some flexibility is, therefore, required.

Time management is based on simple common-sense principles. The first major element in time management is recognising that you put too much pressure on yourself. Remember that most people with time management problems are pressured mainly by themselves and not by others. Taking the pressure off yourself will help you to feel more relaxed so that, in the long run, the susceptibility to anxiety will be decreased.

If you require further information or detail regarding stress management, see my book 'Stress Management: a Guide to Coping with Stress' (Gournay, 1995).

CHAPTER 10: EVALUATING YOUR PROGRESS

How do you know that you are improving? There are several inventories, questionnaires and rating scales that can be used to measure your level of panic or phobia. These usually involve making a rating of how much anxiety you feel in a specific situation or recording your thoughts or reactions to certain objects or situations.

In my view, although such rating scales, questionnaires and inventories can be very helpful for a professional therapist they are less helpful for either the sufferer or a co-therapist. The most reliable way of evaluating your progress is to use your problem and target definitions, and to sit down with a friend, partner or spouse (or co-therapist) and decide how much progress you have made towards the targets that you defined on the basis of your problems.

Furthermore, a simple recording of day-to-day behaviour in the form of a diary is the final arbiter of success. Simply put, if you have a phobia, and you have managed to face the object or situation increasingly often and with decreasing levels of anxiety, you are getting better. If you are still avoiding you are not making progress.

The diary shown on page 62 suggested that you used an anxiety scale ranging from 0-8 to help you to evaluate your progress. However, you should not expect your anxiety ratings to drop dramatically but, if you are facing the phobic situation regularly, your initial rating should gradually drop, for example from 7 to 6, 6 to 5 and so on and with each exposure. The time taken to feel a reduction in anxiety should become increasingly smaller. There will, however, always be exceptions to this so do not be worried if you experience an occasional surge in anxiety or if you have an occasional exposure where your anxiety level remains high.

If after say 10 exposures, there is no real reduction in your anxiety you need to think again about whether your exposure is being properly carried out. One common reason for failing to make progress is that your sessions may not be long enough. Lengthening your exposure is the first obvious strategy.

There are, however, other reasons for lack of progress and occasionally one hears of sufferers who make progress with some aspects of their problem but not with others. If this is the case, simply change the focus of your exposure, perhaps concentrating for a while on those parts of your plan that are more successful and returning to the more difficult part(s) when you have had more success.

It is also worthwhile discussing progress with your co-therapist or, if you are a member of a self-help organisation, with your contact. This is often helpful. Although exposure is a simple procedure it can sometimes benefit from some objective outside help.

Use the section on problem-and-target definition (Chapter 7) and construct, from the examples provided, a suitable diary or diaries that you can use as your on-going measure(s).

To summarise, you need to evaluate your progress by looking at your original targets. Take each of these in turn and assess how much progress you have made. Don't worry too much if you are doing better in some areas than in others. If there is a particular sticking point leave it alone for a while and return to it later. You should expect some improvement in your anxiety ratings. However, assume that progress may be slow and there will be occasional times when you will experience setbacks.

Overall, the central message here is that you must persist with exposure and try to keep to your plan. Don't be afraid to reconsider your list of problems and targets (with the help of your co-therapist if appropriate) and adjust and plan for action accordingly.

Conclusion

Anxiety is probably best seen as an integral part of the human condition. Panic and phobias are so common in the general population that professional help for all sufferers will never be possible, even with the most utopian of health care systems.

Self-help is a greatly under-rated way of tackling these difficulties and this book has set out to suggest some central methods of achieving this. As I have repeated over and over again, exposure to one's fear is essential for successful self-treatment. The way that you set about facing your fear is a very individual matter. Some people can do this quickly and others more slowly.

Some of the suggestions I have made may not suit all sufferers. Take what you find useful from this short text. If some of my suggestions are not helpful, leave them to one side but do not use this as a reason for discarding any of the central principles. Whatever your anxiety remember that a persistent approach will eventually work provided that you keep the principles that I have described above firmly in your sights.

REFERENCES

American Psychiatric Association, 1994, Diagnostic and Statistical Manual IV, American Psychiatric Association, New York.

Brown G. W., Harris T., 1995, Life Events and Illness: A Handbook for the Caring Professions, Unwin Hyman: International Thomson, London.

Gournay K. J. M., 1989, Agoraphobia: Current Perspectives on Theory and Treatment, Routledge, London.

Gournay K., 1995, Stress Management: a Guide to Coping with Stress, Asset Books, Leatherhead, Surrey.

Gournay K. J. M., Brooking J. I., 1994, Community Psychiatric Nurses in Primary Care, British Journal of Psychiatry **165**: 231-238.

Marks I. M., 1978, Living with Fear, McGraw Hill, London.

FURTHER READING

Marks I. M., 1987, Fears, Phobias and Rituals, Oxford Publications London.
This is the definitive text on the subject and, although it is nine years old, it is still perhaps the best book of its kind. It describes in detail all of the clinical syndromes and provides a scholarly overview of both theory and treatment.

Sheldon B., 1995, Cognitive Behavioural Therapy, Routledge London.
This is an excellent up-to-date account of cognitive behavioural treatments which, although written for health professionals, would provide the sufferer with a good overview of the philosophy underpinning behavioural treatment and a very helpful account of various theories written in a readable fashion.

Rachman S., Wilson G., 1980, The Effects of Psychological Therapy, Pergamon Press, London.
This is a book written for the lay person as well as the professional and examines the issue of effectiveness of psychological treatments. In particular it addresses the differences between psychoanalytically based treatments and behavioural methods and examines the evidence regarding effectiveness.

OTHER RESOURCES AND SOURCES OF HELP

Action on Smoking and Health (ASH)

109, Gloucester Place, London W1H 4EJ.
Telephone: 0171-935 -3519

Alcoholics Anonymous

P. O. Box 1, Stonebow House, Stonebow, York YO1 2NJ.
Telephone: 01904-644026/7/8/9

Biofeedback

Maxwell Cade Foundation, 9, Chatsworth Road, London NW2 4BJ.
Telephone: 0181-451-0083

British Association for Behavioural and Cognitive Psycho-therapy,

The Old Church Hall, 89a, Quicks Road, Wimbledon London SW19 1EX.
Telephone: 0181-715-1725

British Association for Counselling

1, Regent Place, Rugby, Warwicks CV21 2PJ.
Telephone: 01788-758328

Centre for Stress Management

156, Westcombe Hill, Blackheath, London SE3 7HP.
Telephone: 0181-293-4114

Council for Acupuncture

179, Gloucester Place, London NW1 6DX.
Telephone: 0171 - 724 - 5756

No Panic

93, Brands Farm Way, Randlay, Telford, Shropshire TF3 2JQ
Telephone: 01952 - 590005 (Office); 01952 - 590545 (Help-Line)

Triumph over Phobia

P O Box 1831, Bath BA1 3YX.
Telephone: 01225 - 330353

TELEPHONE HELPLINES

Alcoholics Anonymous Helpline

Telephone: 0171-352-3001

No Panic Helpline

Telephone: 01952-590545

SANELINE (information and support for carers, sufferers or friends)

Telephone: 0171-724-8000

SMOKERS QUITLINE

Telephone: 0171-487-3000

IF YOU HAVE ENJOYED THIS BOOK AND FOUND IT HELPFUL WHY NOT TRY ANOTHER ASSET BOOK?

Also by Kevin Gournay

STRESS MANAGEMENT: A GUIDE TO COPING WITH STRESS

We all have to cope with the stress of daily living. Some of us can handle the situation without undue difficulty but, for some, the problems are seem to be insuperable and as a consequence many different side effects become apparent. Sleeplessness, irritability, ulcers, and depression are only some of the common symptoms experienced by those who are vulnerable. What is the difference between those who manage and those who succumb?

Professor Gournay provides, in this easy-to-read guide, an understandable analysis of the root causes of the problems and provides a range of practical solutions which readers can use to overcome their problems. It is written by one of the country's leading experts and so does not contain unproven quackery but provides sound and well-tested advice based on years of experience in leading hospitals in dealing with cases which had become acute. This book provides real assistance to sufferers helps in preventing the need for professional help.

ISBN 1 9001 79 00 8

Available from all good booksellers or directly from Asset Books.

Order your copy today!

ALSO FROM ASSET BOOKS:

YOUR PROBLEM OR MINE? HOW TO DEAL WITH 'DIFFICULT' PEOPLE'

Anne Mulhall

In an era when those in paid employment are shouldering more responsibility and working longer hours the pressure to 'perform', to be 'perfect', is overwhelming. Not surprisingly this is creating a hostile work culture in which 'difficult' people are increasingly encountered. But who are these 'difficult' people? Why are they difficult? Can we learn to deal with them?

Anne Mulhall explores these questions, looking at the ways in which we think about, and act, in difficult relationships and offers a 'menu' of suggestions and ideas through which we can construct a personal strategy for dealing with 'difficult' people in a way that is compatible how we think and act, *our* model, which works for us.

ISBN 1 9001 7901 6

'TO THINE OWN SELF BE TRUE': A GUIDE TO ASSERTIVENESS IN THE WORKPLACE

Sue Holmes

The considerable changes in the working environment have created unprecedented pressures which can, at times, be overwhelming. This is creating a hostile environment where it can be difficult to stand up for yourself in the face of hostile or aggressive behaviour from colleagues and superiors. Assertive behaviour is a way of coping with such situations and allowing us to live with ourselves.

This book explores such issues providing suggestions as to how the pressures can be overcome. It offers many suggestions that can be tried as well as ideas for practice through which each person will be able to develop their skills in the way that works for best for them.

ISBN 1 9001 7901 4

ASSET BOOKS

Practical solutions to everyday problems

USE THIS FORM TO ORDER YOUR COPIES TODAY!

No.	Title	Price	
	Gournay - Stress management: A guide to coping with stress ISBN 1 9001 7900 8	5	95
	Gournay - 'No panic': A practical guide to managing panic and phobia ISBN 1 9001 7903 2	8	50
	Mullhall - 'Your problem or mine?' How to deal with difficult people ISBN 1 9001 7901 6	5	95
	Holmes - 'To thine own self be true': A guide to assertiveness in the workplace ISBN 1 9001 7902 4	6	95
	Postage and Packing	1	00
	TOTAL TO PAY		

Name: ....

Address: ....

....

.... **Postcode:** ....

Please allow 28 days for delivery

Alternatively, please write to:

Asset Books,
PO Box 36,
Leatherhead,
Surrey KT22 8YG.